Famous and Fabulous

DOGS

text by Bernard Barbuk illustrations by John Glover

Famous and Fabulous
DOGS

text by Bernard Barbuk illustrations by John Glover

Peter Lowe

List of Stories

Casebound edition with jacket
ISBN 0 85654 004 8

Casebound edition with picture boards
ISBN 0 85654 008 0

This book is distributed to the wholesale trade in the UK, Australia and New Zealand by Sandle Brothers Limited

Printed in Belgium by Henri Proost & Co, Turnhout

Introduction

You probably already know of the dog as man's best friend—but did you know that dogs were probably man's *first* friends, too?

Centuries before our ancestors learned how to tame horses, or herd reindeer, cattle, sheep or goats, the dog had become the trusted friend and helper of hunters and warriors alike. Dogs guarded caves and shelters while the men slept—ever alert to danger, whether it came from human enemies or wild animals. And dogs were the first animals man used to carry burdens and pull weights.

From those far-off times right through to the present day, dogs have shared in all our triumphs and disasters—increasing our happiness or easing our disappointment and misery.

Today there are many different breeds of dogs all over the world, from the tiny chihuahua to the elegant afghan hound and the giant great dane. Some are dogs specially bred for hunting, some are used for guarding property or herding sheep; many are now kept just as pets.

It is quite possible that you already have a dog of your own. Probably he will never get the chance to behave in the heroic way that many of the dogs in this book do. But remember that whatever kind of dog he is, he has his own special needs and that as he is now a domestic animal, living with you in a house or a flat, he depends on you a lot.

It is up to you to see that he is properly fed—with the right kinds of food—that he has plenty of exercise, and that his coat is kept clean and tidy. By having him vaccinated by the vet when he is a puppy, you can also save him from several painful and dangerous diseases.

You have certainly seen photographs or films of the way in which carefully trained dogs—police dogs, guide dogs or sheep dogs—can help their owners. Of course your own dog does not need to reach such a high standard; but with a little patience you can easily teach him to understand what you want him to do.

The story of man and the story of dogs are closely woven together. Indeed, the history of one is really the history of the other. For if dogs are devoted to man, and depend on him, where would man be without his first and best friend? Perhaps man owes his very survival as a species to his friend the dog, who protected him across thousands of dark, vulnerable years.

One of the ways in which the human race is unique is in its ability to tame, domesticate and make friends with other creatures—of which, of course, the dog was the very first. In this book, you will read some of the ways in which this friendship has proved itself.

Bernard Barbuk

CAMPIGLIA
MARITTIMA

Lampo the traveller

Many dogs like to travel, but in Italy there once lived a dog who liked it more than anything else. The first sight that anyone had of him at the little railway station of Campiglia Marittim, where travellers for Elba leave the Turin-Rome railway line, was when he jumped down from a freight train from Leghorn. "He" was a medium-sized white-and-brown mongrel, with a remarkably self-assured air, and he wasted no time before getting himself a big drink of water and making a tour of inspection.

He seemed particularly impressed with Elvio the under-stationmaster's office, and after selecting a cool spot, he contentedly settled down and went to sleep. Elvio didn't know it, but he had been "adopted".

It was only a day or so before the dog had a name: Lampo. Lampo is Italian for "flash", and the men called him that because of the way he rushed around inspecting everything —particularly the trains as they entered and left—and generally acted as the self-appointed watchdog and superintendent of the station.

But that wasn't all that Lampo did. He was a traveller: a natural traveller, a born traveller. Above all, he was a traveller who loved trains. Elvio found this out very soon after Lampo had arrived, when he took the train home to the little country town of Piombino where he lived, a short way up the line. It wasn't until the train was under way that Elvio realized that Lampo had come too—uninvited, until that moment unseen, and certainly without a ticket.

It soon turned out that Lampo liked visiting Elvio's home. He liked Elvio's wife, and he liked Mirna, Elvio's little daughter, even more. In fact, he took to visiting them at every hour of the day. In particular he could always be relied upon to be at Elvio's house first thing in the morning to take Mirna to her nursery school; and, when he spent the evenings with the family, he always remembered to catch the last train back to the station at night.

It soon appeared that Lampo knew the railway timetables rather better than anyone else on the railway. Not only did he never miss a train, but he soon began to take trips all around the region too. He would set off early in the morning—after seeing Mirna safely to school, of course—and no one would see or hear anything more of him for the rest of the day, and sometimes for the night too. But somehow, no matter where he had been or how many changes of train it had required, he always managed to be there to take Mirna to school again the next morning.

Lampo very soon developed another habit that endeared him to everyone on the railway. The cooks on the restaurant cars of the express trains began to feed Lampo with leftover pieces of meat. At first he ran up the platform barking when the expresses stopped, until he got his reward from the chef; but soon he took to just strolling casually up to the restaurant car and looking up at the window until the chef's head appeared. Then, instead of eating everything he was given, he began to store some for the days when he got nothing.

Lampo never missed the arrival of an express—unless he was away on one of his trips, of course. He would be lying dozing in Elvio's office when suddenly, before anyone else had heard anything, he would prick his ears and wake up. Sure enough, a few minutes later, the express would roar into the station.

One day Lampo went away on his longest trip so far. He was seen boarding the Leghorn-Pisa-Spezia-Genoa express. Everyone was very worried: it was one thing for him to travel around on the local trains, but the fast expresses were another matter. Where would he end up? How would he ever find his way back?

Elvio telephoned every station on the line: nowhere had there been any sign of Lampo. But, in the morning, there he was waiting outside Elvio's house as usual, looking none the worse.

Another day: another trip. This time the station at Civitavecchia telephoned. Lampo was there—should they send him back?

"No, don't worry," said Elvio, who was begining to understand Lampo very well. "He'll get the train back on his own when he feels like it. Lampo doesn't like being helped."

As time went on, Lampo visited all the railway stations within 200 miles of Campiglia. Any train would do—except goods trains which he seemed to have an aversion to. Every day he visited new farms, new villages, new towns. Railwaymen fastened used tickets around his neck, or bits of paper with "Free pass for Lampo, the travelling dog" written on them.

The fact was, however, that they were only *imitation* free passes. Lampo was breaking the rules, and although most people on the railway were prepared to ignore it, a few were not. To them Lampo—an unaccompanied dog on a train—was a dangerous nuisance. Something must be done.

One day Elvio was called to the stationmaster's office and told to stop Lampo travelling. Stop Lampo travelling! That wasn't going to be easy. Elvio decided to take Lampo away from the station, to his own home. "Perhaps that way he'll lose the travelling habit," he thought.

Naturally, life wasn't the same for Lampo away from the trains, and several times he tried to go for a trip. But the railwaymen, under strict orders, put him off. All the same, the railway staff missed him, and so did nearly everyone else who travelled regularly on the railway—especially the children.

In the end, Lampo was allowed to go back to the station; and for a time he seemed to have learned his lesson. But it couldn't last—and this time there were to be no half-measures. Lampo had to go. He was packed off in the luggage van of the Naples express, and the guard had instructions, when they reached Naples, to put him on another express going even further away.

So Lampo went—taking with him, it seemed, the happiness of everyone who had known him. Five gloomy winter months passed.

Then, one day, as Elvio was working in his office, he heard a great uproar in the station. A man burst into his office. "Come outside quick!" he shouted. "Lampo's back!"

It was true. But the Lampo who returned was barely recognizable as the same dog that had left five months before. His shiny white-and-brown coat was covered with dirt, and had bald, raw patches. He could barely walk, for his paws were cracked and bleeding; his neck was swollen and bruised and round it someone had twisted a crude wire "collar" to which was attached a piece of frayed string; and Lampo was very thin.

In only one thing was he unchanged: in his love of the railway. He had returned on the Rome express!

"Get Lampo back in condition," the

stationmaster told Elvio. "He's to stay here—always."

At first it looked as if it was too late. Lampo was ill. He collapsed; he couldn't swallow; he burned with a fever. The vet came—and left again. He said there was no hope. Yet Lampo did not die! Next morning he was a little better, the day after he was stronger still, and very soon he was his old self again. And far from being put off by his experiences, he seemed to like travelling more than ever.

However, there was a difference now. For Lampo started to become famous. It began among the railwaymen and the regular travellers—the station telephone never stopped ringing. Always there was someone else asking for news of Lampo. Was he better? What had he done today? Where had he gone? What had he eaten? How had he found his way home after his long absence?

The newspapers began writing about him too. At first it was just the local newspapers, then the big papers in Rome and Turin took up the story. A television company even made a film about him.

One day, the great mystery of where Lampo had come from years before, was solved. An old man, looking rather annoyed, got off the train at Campiglia. "I've missed my stop," he complained to Elvio. "I wanted to get off at Leghorn but I missed it." Then he caught sight of Lampo. Suddenly his face broke into a delighted smile.

"Hello, old boy, do you remember me?"

Lampo looked and sniffed, then looked and sniffed again. He did remember the old man! For Lampo had once been the old man's dog. Bigheri, the old man called him, Bigheri the American, because before belonging to the old man he had belonged to a sailor on an American ship. One day the ship had sailed and Lampo (or Bigheri) had been nowhere to be found, and had been left behind. The old man was the harbour watchman and he had looked after Lampo until the day when Lampo had been chased into the railway yard by the town dog-catcher, who was rounding up stray dogs. Some railwaymen, feeling sorry for him, had flung him into a freight truck to save him.

It seemed only right to Elvio that the old man should have Lampo back, and the two of them set off together happily enough. But four days later Lampo was back—he had obviously missed the railway. However, he was a kind and faithful dog, as well as a clever one, and from that day until the old man died Lampo used to make occasional trips to Leghorn to see him.

Lampo himself was beginning to get old. As time went by—and he had now lived for eight years at the station—he spent more and more of his time sleeping. He did less and less travelling, and finally he stopped altogether. He couldn't even take Mirna to school any more, and during the autumn and winter he was sick.

If you had been in the small station that had become Lampo's home on a certain day that next summer, you would have seen a crowd gathered around an engine. It was quite a big crowd and it grew bigger every moment. But there was none of the laughing or talking you expect of Italian crowds. For Lampo lay dead under the wheels of the train.

What had happened? Had he tried one last adventure, risking—and losing—his life for one last trip on his beloved railway? Had his strength failed as he ran across the tracks in front of the train? Was life without adventure not worth living?

No one will ever know the exact details of his death, but many people all over the world remember his life. So if you happen to be passing through Campiglia Marittim on the way to Rome or Turin, or perhaps going to Elba on holiday, keep a lookout for Lampo—there is a statue of him there, under a laburnum tree where he once loved to sit in the summer heat; and maybe Elvio will be there to tell you about him.

Dragon remembers his master

Everyone agreed they made a handsome trio: the young chevalier, Aubrey de Montdidier, the beautiful Isabelle de Villenomble whom he was going to marry, and Dragon, the splendid deerhound who was the young man's faithful friend and companion.

They became quite famous. Isabelle was a lady-in-waiting at the court of Charles, the King of France, and Aubrey was a captain in the royal guard. Wherever they were seen—at court or in a public place—people would point them out and follow them down the street. For the handsome young soldier and his fiancée were very popular with everyone, and, then as now, most people liked dogs.

But there was one person who most definitely did not wish them well: Captain Macaire.

He, like Aubrey, was a captain in the royal guard, and for months he had competed with Aubrey for Isabelle's love. When he found that he had lost and she preferred the other man, instead of taking it gracefully (if sadly) as most men would have done, he began to hate the young man who had been chosen instead of him.

"Vengeance! vengeance! I will be avenged!" he muttered to himself, hour after hour, day after day, night after night.

In fact, he made up his mind to kill his rival. He soon discovered that this was more easily said than done, for everywhere Aubrey went Dragon went too. Moreover, Macaire's chances in a fair fight were none too good anyway, since Aubrey was by far the better swordsman. But, of course, a fair fight was the very last thing Macaire had in mind . . .

It was the autumn of the year 1361; the place was the forest of Bondy. Aubrey was riding through the forest with his faithful hound cantering a few yards ahead of him. The trees were large, and beneath them the bushes and undergrowth were dense and thickly clustered. They came to a bend in the road, and for just one moment Dragon was lost to view. In that moment someone hidden in the bushes by the road clubbed Dragon down; the same person then stepped out in front of the horse and, while Aubrey was still too startled to defend himself, stabbed him with a hunting spear.

Hours later Dragon awoke, his head aching, his long legs scarcely able to support the weight of his body. Weakly he tottered off to find his master.

Aubrey was nowhere to be seen, but Dragon easily found his track through the dead leaves and grass of the forest floor. It was a broad track, easy enough for a man, let alone a dog, to follow: the sort of track left when someone is dragged by the heels. It led to a newly dug grave among the under-

growth, thinly covered by fallen leaves.

What should Dragon do? Leave Aubrey and fetch help? Go back to Paris?

Dragon seemed to consider each possibility in turn. No, he decided, he would not leave his beloved master, not yet. However, help was certainly needed, and somehow it had to be found.

So Dragon began to howl: the full-blooded, long, deep, musical howl of a deerhound in full voice.

The eerie cry was heard for miles around. It echoed in and over every valley and every hill. But no one came. For two whole days Dragon never once left off crying for help; and for two whole days the local people cowered in their homes in superstitious terror of the ghost or devil whose voice pealed so loudly and unceasingly.

Then, all at once, it stopped. Dragon had left his master's grave and was running off as fast as he could towards Paris.

After many hours Dragon finally came to Isabelle's house. There he began to howl once again, outside the heavy wooden front door. Luckily Isabelle chose that moment to look out of her window to see what was causing all the commotion, and of course she recognized Dragon at once.

"Let him in—it's Dragon, the chevalier's dog," she cried.

So the servants opened the great door, stood aside, and, in the cobbled courtyard of the house, Dragon and Isabelle met. Gently she stroked his head.

"Heavens, do you see? He's been hurt!" she cried aloud. "Something has happened—something terrible—I know it."

Dragon licked her face and hands; then he began to pull gently at the hem of her fur-edged gown. First he pulled then turned and looked back at her, then pulled again.

Isabelle understood in a moment.

"He wants me to follow!" she cried. "And I will. Come, two men shall go with me. Fetch me my cloak, and bring horses."

Along the dusty roads they went, never stopping for rest or food until they reached the first outlying trees of the forest. A brief halt; then they went on again, deep into the woods to the spot where Dragon knew his young master lay . . .

In the sad, sad days that followed, Dragon went to live in Isabelle's house, but neither dog nor girl forgot the handsome young man who had been so dear to both of them.

One day Isabelle, now dressed totally in black, was walking slowly through a Paris street accompanied by Dragon, when a company of royal guards came marching by. At their head rode Macaire, his curved and fluted armour glittering in the sun, his horse's bridle clinking, and the tall white plume on his helmet bobbing with the movement of his great chestnut horse.

He and his men were a marvellous sight, and dozens of people flocked to watch them as they passed; others leaned from the windows of their houses to get a better view.

But something happened which spoilt the splendour of it all. Suddenly, without any warning except for a low growl of the deepest hatred, Dragon hurtled forward, leaped up to the saddle, and dragged the glorious rider down to the dirty cobbles.

In a moment a dozen strong hands had pulled the hound away, and if it had not been for Isabelle Dragon might well have been killed by the soldiers.

"No, leave him, leave him," Isabelle cried. "He is my dog! I can't understand why he did that: he's always so mild. Excuse us, Captain Macaire, but Dragon and I have both recently suffered a great loss. Good day, sir."

The affair did not end there, however. Hundreds of people had seen what had happened, and news of the hound's attack spread rapidly through the town. Quite a number of those who heard of it already knew that Dragon had been Aubrey's dog and that Macaire and Aubrey had been bitter rivals. So the story spread even faster and began to take on another tone.

"Strange, is it not, that Aubrey's dog should attack the man who vowed vengeance on his master?"

"Strange indeed—especially as Aubrey was murdered!"

At last, the story reached the ear of the king himself—Charles the Good, as he was called.

"There is probably nothing in it," he said quietly, "but I must be sure. Send for Captain Macaire, and for Isabelle de Villenomble, and that hound too!"

When Macaire was brought before him, the king told him to hide himself behind the large crowd of courtiers. Then, when he was totally hidden, King Charles ordered Isabelle and Dragon to enter.

Slowly, with downcast eyes, Isabelle walked across the smooth marble floor of the throne room. Slowly, and with great dignity, Dragon followed at her heel—that is, until he got half-way towards the throne. For then, with another vicious growl, he leaped forward, straight at the group of courtiers.

Lords and ladies were flung right and left as the dog bundled them aside. He was only interested in one man: the one whose hated scent he had detected among everyone else's.

Once again the hound was dragged away from Macaire, just as his teeth were snapping at the wretched man's throat.

"This dog is vicious! Mad! It should be killed!" cried Macaire.

"Is it vicious? Is it indeed mad?" asked the king. "It appears to be vicious towards nobody but the captain here."

"Your Majesty, Dragon has always been the mildest and gentlest of hounds," said Isabelle. "He has never attacked anybody—except for Captain Macaire, and he has only done that since his dear master, the chevalier Aubrey de Montdidier, was brutally murdered."

"Does the lady speak the truth about the dog?" King Charles asked his courtiers.

They nodded eagerly in agreement.

"Did the dog ever behave badly towards Macaire while Montdidier lived?" he asked.

The courtiers shook their heads.

"I see. Then it seems, Captain Macaire, that this dog accuses you of murder. Not quite a case for the courts, I think, so I proclaim that you and the dog shall meet in combat—I have no doubt that if you are innocent, Fate will be on your side."

So it was arranged. An arena was built in the centre of the city, and dog and man met in battle.

Macaire was armed with a great club of spiked wood and he wore full armour. Dragon had no weapons except his teeth, and he was provided with a large barrel for a refuge to retire to if he needed.

The soldiers could hardly hold Dragon back. As soon as the signal was given to begin, he hurtled across the arena, and flew straight at Macaire's throat. Macaire was ready for him, though, and brought the great club down in one devastating blow.

Somehow, in mid-air, Dragon twisted aside, and before Macaire could strike again, the hound was on him!

A cry went up from the crowd as the great dog tore savagely at the man's throat. Macaire was shouting something, and although once again men ran to pull Dragon away, this time there was a difference: Macaire was shouting his confession, and he was rescued from the teeth of Dragon only to die on the gallows of the public executioner.

The story of Montdidier's dog is 600 years old and is one of the most famous and often-repeated dog stories in European literature. Though there are many slightly different versions of it, it is said to be true. True or not, it illustrates very well one important part of a dog's character: the ability to remember enemies (as well as friends) over long periods, and to be quite unforgiving towards those guilty of the worst crime in a dog's eyes—a crime against its master.

Bruno's last rescue

Bruno was every inch a St. Bernard—a real St. Bernard, that is, not one of the fat, short-winded, long-haired sort that are bred just for dog shows.

Bruno was a rescue dog, one of the finest ever to be born in the famous monastery in the St. Bernard pass, which crosses the Alps between Switzerland and Italy. He was enormously strong, with a white and tawny-brown coat, a short muzzle, quick intelligent eyes, and an almost miraculous ability to detect the faintest cry or scent.

That year, the last of Bruno's life, autumn closed in early with sudden, dangerous mists; then came the first of the snowfalls and the first rescues of the "season".

Other dogs than Bruno did the rescuing. For Bruno, brave fellow, had reached the age of retirement, and now spent most of his time dozing by the fire near Brother Anselm, his handler and special friend.

Brother Anselm had shared many of Bruno's greatest rescues. Often he had followed Bruno with food and medicine, or, with another member of the Order, had taken a stretcher to bring in an injured person whom Bruno had found. Now both dog and man were thought to be too old for rescue work.

"Ah, Bruno, Bruno—our rescuing days are over now," Brother Anselm said quietly, patting his old friend's smooth, warm forehead. "Thirty-nine rescues! What a record you have, old friend. Yet it's a pity you never had the chance to make it a round forty. Still, it's too late now."

Little did he know that Bruno's fortieth rescue was about to begin.

A few miles from the monastery, across the border in Italy, lived a boy called Pietro, the small son of Guiseppe the shepherd. Pietro's family was very, very poor; and his mother was sick. So, that spring, he and his father had left their home to work in Switzerland. All that summer they had worked in the high pastures of the Bernese

Alps, guarding the sleek Swiss cows, and saving their money to take home at the end of the summer.

It had been a lonely life, but at least they had each other for company—which is why Pietro's mother had made her husband take the little boy with him.

"But you will be all alone here without him," Guiseppe had protested.

"I know, Guiseppe, I know. But you will need him more, all by yourself in the mountains," his wife had replied. "All I ask is that you bring him home safely."

So the two had set off for the high Alpine pastures. Here the grass was as green as emeralds and studded with white, red, pink, blue and purple flowers. Right on the very snow line grew tiny grey-white edelweiss—of all flowers the ones Pietro loved best.

It had been a fine summer. The cows were fat and mild-tempered, and when they moved the bells round their necks chimed softly so that Guiseppe and Pietro were always able to find them, even if they were hidden in a fold of the ground or by a sudden bank of mist.

Guiseppe looked up at the weather anxiously. He and little Pietro didn't have far to go, but the St. Bernard pass could be very dangerous—and Guiseppe was troubled.

"The bad weather is coming early this year," he thought. "But it seems bright enough just now, and it won't get any better for delaying."

So they set off, walking steadily and carrying enough food in their bags to last the journey.

To begin with, everything went well and they made good time, for the mountain turf was springy, and the air was clean and perfumed with the grass and flowers.

But Guiseppe kept glancing up at the sky apprehensively. He was worried, and with good reason. Presently he began to frown. For the bright cloudless sky of the morning had changed, and now the sun was only fitfully gleaming through dark-brown clouds. Then the mist began to roll in, and with it came a piercing, deadly cold.

Guiseppe stopped: he had been wrong to set out! They were both now in deadly danger.

"Quick Pietro," he said, "button your coat. We are going back. A storm is coming and this is no place to be caught in the open!"

Together they hurried back the way they had come, the little boy trying hard to keep up with his long-striding father.

"Hurry son—you must hurry," Guiseppe said anxiously.

"I know, Father. I'm doing my best," Pietro answered. "But perhaps the weather will improve."

"It will get worse before it gets better," said Guiseppe. "See: the sky is almost purple now. We shall be caught in the storm! We must get back to the chalet!"

But it was too late, and they had only gone a little way further on when the storm broke. It seemed as if all the snow in the world was suddenly being emptied upon them in smothering, choking, blinding clouds.

"Faster, faster!" grunted Guiseppe from between clenched teeth.

But little Pietro could not go any faster. The darkness frightened him and he was tired. Gradually his feet began to drag, and his arms to drop, till they hung at his sides.

"Faster son—keep going," said Guiseppe again, pulling the boy along. But little Pietro now began to stumble at every step; sleep was creeping over him.

"Father, father, I'm so sleepy," the boy mumbled.

Guiseppe couldn't hear him—but he didn't have to. He could see Pietro's condition well enough.

"You MUST NOT SLEEP!" he cried, shaking Pietro by the shoulders.

"I *must*," sighed Pietro. "The snow is so warm, Papa, so very, very warm, and soft.

Let me sleep for a few minutes, Papa."

For Pietro the world had become one hissing, sifting, swirling sea of whiteness—snow was over him and around him: he was swimming in snow, floating in snow, spiralling down in snow, turning, spinning round in snow . . . He slumped to the ground.

Guiseppe hauled Pietro to his feet and lifted him on to his back. Then he struggled on, carrying his son. He soon had to stop: in the deep snow, bitter cold and high wind, even Pietro's small weight was too much for his father.

"Just a moment, Pietro," Guiseppe said. I'll just rest for a bit, then we'll carry on."

But at the very moment Guiseppe set his son down there came a sudden gust of wind, filled, it seemed, with the stored-up strength of the whole storm.

In an instant Pietro was torn from his father's arms—and swept away. Away into the blinding whiteness tumbling over and over down a steep white snow bank, quite beyond Guiseppe's sight or his power to follow.

At that moment too, safe within the strong walls of the monastery, Bruno raised his head, listening intently. He was the only dog left in the monastery: all the others were already at work in the storm. Now he sprang to his feet, showing not a trace of old age.

"What—another rescue, another journey?" cried old Brother Anselm. "It seems you will make your fortieth rescue after all. Alas, how I wish I could come with you, but unlike you, old friend, I really am too old."

Moments later Bruno was off: bounding through the snow as fast as in the great days of his youth. As he ran the storm suddenly died away, and a deep brooding silence descended over the whole St. Bernard pass.

Somewhere in all that deep white silence lay little Pietro, a tiny figure buried in a snowdrift, sleeping deeply and gradually slipping away from life.

Somewhere too lay Guiseppe, overcome by exhaustion, cold and bitter remorse at having lost his little boy in the storm. But for Guiseppe rescue was only minutes away, as a team of monks on patrol in the snow were about to stumble across him.

Pietro, on the other hand, had been tumbled by the wind far from any path, and out of sight of even the keenest-eyed searcher.

Who knows what marvellous combination of senses Bruno used to find Pietro? But find him he did, locating where under the smooth surface of the snow the child lay, and burrowing with furious efficiency until he had uncovered the boy's body. Veteran of so many rescues as he was, Bruno was in no doubt over what he should do next.

Quickly he stretched himself over Pietro, warming the freezing child with his own body, and licking the cold face with his hot tongue.

Slowly and painfully Pietro was dragged back to consciousness—away from the deceptive, deadly warmth of his dreams to agonizingly cold reality. At last he opened his eyes and gazed slowly into those of the great St. Bernard.

Bruno now crouched down by the boy's side, inviting him to climb on his back. Dimly Pietro understood and hauled himself on to the dog's great back, clutching his thick fur with all his remaining strength.

Then Pietro slept again. He would never know how the old dog fought his way through the deep snow, how he found a path where there was none, how he pushed his tired old body onwards to the very door of the monastery. There, with a bump, Bruno rolled the child gently on to a stretcher.

Then Pietro opened his eyes again—and there was old Brother Anselm smiling at him; and Guiseppe too, wrapped in blankets and laughing and crying all at once; and there also was the great old dog who had rescued him.

Bruno had saved his fortieth life; that done, and his life-work over, the old dog quietly laid himself down and died.

Flush, a writer's companion

And if one or two quiet tears
Dropped upon his glossy ears,
Or a sigh came double,
Up he sprang in eager haste
Fawning, fondling, breathing fast,
In a tender trouble.

Many famous authors have had dogs whose names have been remembered for ever through their works. But no writer's dog has ever been better-known than Flush, the cocker spaniel of Elizabeth Barrett Browning, the poetess. Not only did Flush's mistress write a number of poems about Flush, but the little dog is unique in having had his biography written by another famous writer—Virginia Woolf.

Yet, in many ways, Flush did not have an adventurous life. He never did anything very heroic: he avenged no crimes; he performed no mighty deeds of endurance or intelligence; he did not influence history in any way whatsoever. He was just Flush—the loving companion of his mistress. In fact, of all the famous dogs of history, he is the one most like the dogs we all know.

Flush was born over a hundred years ago; he was a rich brown in colour, and in the sunlight seemed to be made of pure gold. His first mistress was another writer, Miss Mitford.

Miss Mitford was very poor. She spent nearly all her time writing essays and book reviews, and short articles for newspapers and magazines.

She would never have sold her beloved Flush, though there were several people who would have paid a good sum for him. But, at last, she gave him away to her dearest friend, who, she felt, needed him more than she did herself.

The friend was Elizabeth Barrett, who lived with her family in Wimpole Street in London.

Elizabeth Barrett was an invalid, though what was wrong with her or whether she was really ill at all is something people do not agree about. It is certain, however, that she spent most of her time in her bedroom; writing and thinking, seeing few people, and eating very little.

When Flush saw those rooms of hers he must have had such a shock. There were none of the country smells and simple homeliness of Miss Mitford's cottage. Instead, he found himself in a gloomy and airless bedroom, crammed with furniture, decorated in dark colours, and smelling chiefly of something quite dreadful which he learned later was called eau-de-Cologne. To Flush's amazement his new mistress seemed to like this smell.

Flush quickly adapted himself to his new life, keeping Miss Barrett company through the long hours of her work and study, and showing her a great deal of love and sympathy. Gone were the days when he could go chasing after rabbits. Now his only outings were a walk in the park—usually on the lead—with Lily Wilson, Miss Barrett's maid, or occasionally a shopping expedition with Miss Barrett and one of her sisters.

Elizabeth knew very well that this was far from being an ideal life for a dog. "A bird in a cage would have as good a story," she wrote in her diary. Yet she also knew that "Flushie is my friend—my companion—and loves me better than he loves the sunshine."

Once or twice a week Miss Barrett had visitors. Not more often because, although she enjoyed the visits of her friends, they exhausted her so much that after them Flush had to eat most of her dinner for her. That is, he had to until one day something happened which seemed to change Miss Barrett's way of looking at life.

It wasn't much in itself, just a letter—but Flush could tell immediately that it was a very important letter. A few days later there was another letter, equally important it seemed, and—Flush guessed rightly—from the same person.

From that time on Flush noticed a definite change in his mistress: she became more interested in the world; she started asking about the weather; she was less content with spending all her days in her room.

What caused this change in her, Flush couldn't guess. Then, one day the problem was solved. Miss Barrett had a visitor. Not one of her old friends; not one of those who left her exhausted and feeble. This was someone Flush had never seen before: a mysterious-looking man, dressed in black, with lemon-yellow gloves, who gave his name as Robert Browning.

Robert Browning was a famous poet, and he talked very earnestly with Elizabeth . . .

Flush did not like Mr. Browning! For after he had gone Miss Barrett did not fall back exhausted on her cushions. Her cheeks glowed, her eyes shone, and she ate every bit of her dinner.

All of a sudden, Flush felt lonely. He was jealous!

Spring came, and Elizabeth had less time for her little dog than before. She went about more now. She went to the drawing-room; she went for walks. She amazed her father (the dour, forbidding Mr. Barrett) and her doctor, and the rest of the family. None of them knew where her strength came from.

But Flush knew. Oh yes! What's more, Flush didn't approve. The next time Mr. Browning came to call, Flush showed him exactly what he thought of him: he bit Mr. Browning.

"Perhaps my mistress will send him away now she knows what I really feel about him," thought the little spaniel hopefully.

But the result of his attack was a sad disappointment to the dog.

For one thing, Mr. Browning took absolutely no notice. Then, after he had gone, his dear kind mistress actually *smacked* him, on the ears. Well, he didn't mind that—at least it showed she had taken notice—but then she ignored him for a long, long time, and that was terrible. Eventually Flush said he was sorry, in his doggy way, and he was forgiven.

Flush wasn't sorry for very long, however, and his forgiveness didn't last either. A week or so later he bit Mr. Browning again. This time it was Wilson the maid who did the smacking, and she also locked him in the kitchen until the Great Man had said his good-byes to Miss Barrett.

Flush's disgrace was complete—for a time. Mr. Browning did his best to win the little dog over, and at last the same strange thing that had happened to Miss Barrett happened to Flush also. He began to love Mr. Browning!

So life went on—simple, ordered, safe, but somehow more exciting. That is, simple, ordered, safe and exciting for Elizabeth. For Flush there was something else: danger. He was stolen.

It was the work of dog thieves who preyed upon the smart districts of London, stealing dogs and demanding ransom for them. If the owners paid the money, they got their dogs back. If not, the dogs were killed. Usually the owners paid.

When Flush was stolen, something

happened to stop the system working, or at least working smoothly. Elizabeth's father did not believe in "giving in" to criminals, not even if they threatened to send Flush's head and paws in a parcel. No! Pay once, he said, and you will have to pay again.

In the Barrett household, everyone did just what Mr. Barrett told them to. He stopped Elizabeth's brother Henry from paying over the ransom money. Indeed, he stopped any member of the family from helping her and she was forced to act herself.

That day nothing could stop Elizabeth. Not fear of her father; not fear of losing the respect of Mr. Browning—who also wished her to resist the demands of the thieves, and who that very day had written proposing marriage; not fear of going from her own safe and comfortable world into the fearful, violent dens of the poor.

"Flush, poor Flush, who has loved me so faithfully; have I the right to sacrifice him in his innocence?" she asked.

So, at last, after five whole days of utter misery, weak from hunger, crawling with lice, desperate with thirst, Flush *was* saved.

Now excitement of a very different kind was on the way to Flush, and to his dear mistress: excitement involving a complete change in both their lives, both their worlds. Change from the over-furnished cosiness of Wimpole Street in damp, foggy London, to the bright sunlight, the warm, dusty streets, the marble and tiles of Italy.

One September day Miss Elizabeth Barrett left the house with Lily Wilson and never came back—that is, she never came back as *Miss* Elizabeth *Barrett*. She *did* come back, and quite quickly too, but she took care to remove the gold wedding ring from her finger before she entered her father's house. She had married Mr. Browning in secret, without her father's consent. No one knew except Wilson, and the secret was kept for a few days more while Elizabeth stayed in Wimpole Street, hurriedly completing her mysterious preparations.

At four o'clock one morning the secret Mrs. Browning rose and dressed. Then, lifting Flush in her arms, she took one long last look at the room that had once been her whole world, and, with her faithful Wilson, slipped quietly downstairs and out of the house to where a cab was waiting.

Fearful still of her father's anger, Elizabeth was eloping.

They all went to Pisa, in Italy and, when the winter was over, to Florence. Everything was so very different for Flush. Florence was sun to be basked in, lizards to watch and chase, marvellous smells of wine and garlic and herbs and olive oil; strange, ill-bred but fascinating dogs to play with.

Things were very different for Mrs. Browning too, and she changed with it. Now she did things that would have amazed her doctor in London. She went for long walks exploring the streets, the palaces and the galleries of the city; she spent long hours scrambling over the mountains; she ate hearty meals and drank wine by the tumbling mountain streams.

One day Flush was surprised by the arrival of an addition to their family circle—a strange and helpless little creature that cried frequently and demanded much of his mistress's attention.

They called him Pen, and Elizabeth and Robert and Wilson fussed and bothered around the baby to a degree that at first amazed the little golden-haired cocker spaniel. The "old" Flush would have been jealous at this sudden rival for his mistress's affections. But the new Flush—the Flush who had accepted Robert Browning, who had the streets to play in and the market people as his friends—the new Flush was above that! Soon, he was fussing and bothering around the infant with the rest.

From then on there were no more great surprises in Flush's life: it went on quietly and happily in his adopted land until one day—oddly unrecorded by the Brownings—Flush quietly died . . .

The dog that joined the navy

Well now, where shall we begin? It's a long story I have to tell, so you had better get comfortable. Let me see. I haven't always been Flax the navy dog of Rävholmnen, you know. Oh dear me no!

My first master was the smith. An enormous man, and if he wasn't the kindest master a dog could have, he wasn't the worst I ever came across either. He could be kind when he wanted to be, and I don't suppose he would have got rid of me if it hadn't been for my habit of chasing things—lambs, people on bicycles, poodles.

I still think it wasn't really my fault. No one bothered to teach me how to behave, you see. Everyone just shouted at me or kicked me when I did something wrong.

Anyway, one day the smith sold me to his senior apprentice, and of all the masters I ever had he was the very worst. At least the others *fed* me. But not him! I had to hunt for everything I ate, and you can't blame a young dog for getting wild under those conditions.

My new master soon passed me on again—to Ole, who wanted a watchdog. In other words, he wanted to have me within sight of the gate of his farm to warn him if anyone came near. He kept me chained in my kennel: all day and all night, summer and winter, with just an hour or so off every day for exercise.

Oh I was certainly a good watchdog: in fact I wasn't far short of being a killer! The only reason I wasn't totally wild was because a lady who worked in the farm kitchen and a young farm labourer called Henrik used to smuggle me a little extra food whenever they could.

One day Henrik unchained me and let me run around loose—but that did no good to either of us. I was quickly chained up again, and Henrik was dismissed from the farm.

Soon I was sold yet again, to Klyn, who used to go round all the farms buying eggs and cheese and selling various odds and ends.

In the first week with Klyn I got a basket to sleep in, a warm blanket, and the worst beating I ever had in my life, in that order. But after that Klyn and I got on well enough. I had a job to do, I wasn't chained up, I had food and a comfortable place to sleep, and someone took notice of me. Unfortunately it didn't last!

One day Klyn took me into town where he left me guarding his bicycle. Well, while I was waiting there someone tried to steal it. I bit him just to teach him a lesson, and then this man—this thief, you know—had the nerve to complain to Klyn about me!

What upset me was that Klyn never even tried to find out the truth.

"I'm going to shoot you, my lad," he said, and he would have too, except that when he took me out to do it he had a heart attack, and dropped down stone dead.

My next master was a definite change for the better. His name was Brante, and he was a policeman. Brante had me enrolled at the police training school, where I made quite an impression. Especially on the trainer's arm: for I had a terrible bite in those days!

Anyway, Brante and I did so well on our country beat that we were promoted to the Stockholm docks.

Things were really tough there, with great gangs of drunken sailors to be "moved on" as the police call it. Even so, I got into trouble for being a bit too rough in return. Then after one incident with a really dangerous criminal, Brante was told to get rid of me. This was a real blow to me, I can tell you, for I liked being a police dog (and later events proved that I gave those toughs no more than they deserved, for I met them all again, years after, as you will see).

I was a full-grown alsatian by then, with a thick double coat which kept out even the worst weather (luckily for me), pricked ears, and this white tip to my tail. My teeth were white in those days—they've gone yellow now with age—and I hadn't yet lost this piece of my ear or picked up this scar down my side.

Anyway, my next job was back in the country, helping a gamekeeper called Drum on a big estate in the north. It was grand to be among those country smells again, even if Drum and I did have to go out at all hours and in all weathers to chase the poachers. To make matters worse, the head gamekeeper was dishonest, and the poachers were just as likely to take a shot at Drum and me if they saw us, as at a deer or grouse.

Drum and I caught up with them in the end, and I had a real battle with their leader. I thought that now Drum and I would be very popular on the estate, but not a bit of it! First Drum left, then the head gamekeeper nearly starved me to death, so finally I ran away.

When I stopped running I found myself on Old Jolly's farm. That was at a place called Oxberg, and he was called Old Jolly as a joke because he never smiled.

As far as I can remember, he never even smiled when I saved him from a maddened cow that would have trampled him to death. In fact, right after that he sold me to his stockman, because, he said, I was obviously good with animals!

So I had yet another job, and yet another master. But he was no stranger—being none other than the same young Henrik who had done me a good turn when I was a watchdog at Ole's farm. He'd gone up a bit in the world since those days; and he had a wife and children.

Most of the animals I had to look after were gentle and good-natured, and never gave me a moment's trouble. But one or two could be difficult, and Ut—one of the bulls—was never less than bad-tempered. At his worst he was simply murderous.

Ut was a young bull, black, with short, sharp horns. He had a nasty habit of coming up quietly behind people and suddenly attacking them without warning. The first time I had to deal with him though, he had some excuse. He had broken out of his meadow and some young idiot on the farm had ridden up behind him on a horse and beaten him on the rump in order, I imagine, to make him go back to his field.

The result was that the young picador went flying off down the road with Ut galloping after him. Just then, two of Henrik's children happened to be coming up the road. I shudder to think what would have happened to them if I hadn't been around to intercept friend Ut!

The next time I had trouble with Ut it was Henrik himself I had to save, and it took a third battle with that wretched animal before Henrik and Old Jolly finally got tired of him and sold him.

Ut had to be shipped off to his new master, so Henrik and I escorted him to Göttenburg and on to the ship. Henrik went off on some business leaving me to watch Ut, in case he turned nasty again and broke loose on the ship. Well, I don't know how it happened, but Henrik never came back. Like a good dog, I stayed were I was, and before I knew what was what I was miles out to sea.

Then I went to explore, and once again ran into some old acquaintances—but acquaintances I could very well have done without.

It was a bunch of troublemakers I had come across when Brante and I were on the dock beat years before. I had been rather tough with them then; now it was their turn.

Of course I never exactly saw them—just smelt them; but there was no doubt about what happened. Suddenly I was grabbed from behind and flung overboard.

For a moment I floundered. There were no lights to be seen, no sign of land, nothing except the ship. So I tried to follow it. But it was travelling too fast for me, so I turned round and tried to choose the direction we had come from—and even for me that wasn't easy in the pitch dark. Then I started swimming properly. Luckily it was summer, because even with my double coat I couldn't have lasted very long in winter.

Anyway, I swam all night and on into the morning, until, just when I was reaching exhaustion, I saw an island in the distance and a raft nearer at hand. There were some rather odd water spouts shooting up around the raft, but I was too tired to take any notice of *them*. I only just managed to haul myself on board.

Actually, the raft was an artillery target, which was being towed on a long rope by a little tug, and the water spouts were caused by the shells from guns mounted on the little island I had noticed. But even if I had known that I couldn't have done anything but what I did. Another minute and I would have drowned.

Here again something happened, or rather *someone* happened, to save me. On the tug was a sergeant whose task it was to observe the target, signal when it was safe or unsafe to fire, report the fall of shot, and so on. This sergeant saw me—a dog from the sea—and though he didn't recognize me, soaking wet as I was, he liked dogs and—totally against his orders—he signalled the gunners to cease fire. Later, when the sailors on the tug pulled me on board, he did recognize me. For it was old Drum, the gamekeeper, doing his military service in the navy, and miraculously on hand to save my life!

Sadly though, our reunion was short-lived, for Drum was punished in a mild way for ordering the cease-fire by being sent to another fort. Happily though, the navy let me stay.

There isn't much more to tell. I've had two adventures since becoming a navy dog.

In the first I saved the fort's commander's daughter, one day when I was ashore on a visit. She had got herself lost in the forest and sprained her ankle as well—and if I hadn't been on hand to do the tracking it would have been days before anyone would have found her.

Then—guess what! Another day when I went ashore I ran into some real old acquaintances: sailors they were, from a certain ship that had once sailed from Göttenburg with a very bad-tempered bull on board! Well, I really sank my teeth into the ringleader of that little crowd, I can tell you! In fact, there was so much fuss that we all ended up at the police station.

There my story began to come out. Then the newspapers picked it up, and soon I was famous all over Sweden.

But time passes, and few people remember me now. Not that it matters—for I've retired, as you might say. I'm getting very old it seems. But why should I worry? I'm in the stud book, I've a crown on my shoulder to show I belong to Sweden, a warm bed, plenty of food, and dozens of friends here at Rävholmnen. What more could any dog want at my time of life?

Greyfriars Bobby

The story of Greyfriars Bobby began in the Scottish city of Edinburgh in the middle of the last century. Wednesday was market day in Edinburgh, and every week on that day hundreds of country people flocked into the city to buy and sell at the shops and stalls. Among them was a farmer from Midlothian, by the name of Gray.

There was nothing particularly remarkable about Mr. Gray, nor—so it seemed—about his dog. It was a shaggy little Skye terrier, the sort whose small size and appealing tousled coat partly disguise the fiery temperament and highly independent spirit that lie beneath. Just how independent, the people of Edinburgh were soon to discover.

Every Wednesday, at exactly one o'clock, when the time-signal gun was fired from the ramparts of the great castle, Mr. Gray and Bobby would leave off whatever buying and selling they happened to be doing and go to lunch.

They always stopped promptly at one, not a minute before or after, and they always went to the same restaurant: Traill's Dining Rooms. This was near the market and sold good, wholesome Scottish food. Not surprisingly, therefore, it was popular with townsfolk and visitors alike, especially on market days. But no other customers of Traill's were as regular in their attendance as Bobby and his master. Year in, year out, whatever the weather or the season, they never missed a single Wednesday.

Mr. Gray would hang up his cape and coat on a hook near the door, lean his stick against the wall, and choose something from the menu. Bobby, meanwhile, would sit contentedly beneath his master's chair. *His* lunch never varied: he would start off with a large bun, and follow this up with a good meaty bone.

In 1858 Mr. Gray died, and was buried in

the churchyard of Greyfriars, Edinburgh. Three days after the funeral, market day came around again. As the echoes of the signal gun were dying away, the customers in Traill's, and indeed Mr. Traill himself, were very taken aback to see a tiny bedraggled figure come into the restaurant: a figure that was the very picture of woe and hunger. It was Bobby!

Mr. Traill recognized him at once, and when the little animal came through the door looking beseechingly up at him, he gave him his usual bun and bone.

Then came a surprise. For instead of sitting down under a table to eat—as he had always done in the past—Bobby carefully picked up the food in his mouth, then dashed out into the street with it.

Next day, at exactly the same time, Bobby turned up again. Once more Mr. Traill gave him a bone and a bun, and once more the dog rushed away with his food.

The following day, after Bobby had turned up for the third time, Mr. Traill followed him. Much to his surprise he found that the place Bobby was hurrying back to was the cemetery. Once there, Bobby sat down near where Mr. Gray was buried, and ate his lunch.

Clearly Bobby had stuck by his master, and only the extremes of hunger could make him leave him for a moment.

Now it must not be thought that the friends and relatives of Bobby's dead master were unaware of what was happening, or indifferent to Bobby's well-being. Far from it!

After the funeral Bobby had gone back to Midlothian with them, and when he ran away they made every effort to find him. They finally succeeded in tracing him to Edinburgh, and went to the city to bring the little dog back. But he ran off a second time. Then a third.

It was no good. Nothing would induce Bobby to leave his master.

Another person who tried, and failed, to overcome Bobby's determination to stay at Greyfriars was the groundkeeper there. The fact was that dogs were not allowed in the cemetery, not even for a moment, on a lead or off it. There was a large painted notice hanging up on the cemetery gates to say so.

Of course, no one expected dogs to be able to read, but that wasn't the point. "Against the rules" meant just what it said—and no one believed more in the rules or tried harder to keep them than the groundkeeper.

Time after time he put Bobby out of the cemetery. But as fast as the little terrier was bundled out through one gate he jumped back in through another, or scrambled back over the wall; and in the end it was the groundkeeper who gave in, not Bobby.

"Aye, it's true—rules are rules, as the saying goes," said the groundkeeper rather ruefully to himself. "But there's an exception to every rule—and I suppose that wee dog is the exception to this one!"

Many other people tried to discourage Bobby too, but all of them failed. They tried for a variety of reasons, in a variety of different ways, but mostly they meant well, and pitied him.

"Come along, Bobby; there's a good boy," they would say. "Come along, good little dog; come home with me. I've got a nice warm basket waiting for you."

But Bobby stayed where he was.

Or they would offer him things to eat and then try to tempt him away: "Look here, Bobby—I've brought you some meat, and some splendid bones. Now why don't you be a good dog and come home with me, eh? You'll be much better off!"

But the little terrier never for one moment wavered. He had made up his mind to stay where he was in the cemetery, and nothing could make him change it. (Not that he refused to take the food, of course. Bobby may have been stubborn, but he was certainly not stupid.)

Of course he understood what everyone was trying to tell him: he knew better than anyone just how cold, windy, wet, uncomfortable and (for the most part) lonely Greyfriars churchyard could be. But he was prepared to put up with it.

To make life a little more pleasant for himself, Bobby made his own personal retreat under a fallen tombstone near where Mr. Gray was buried, and he used to shelter there when the weather outside got too bad for him to bear. Things got even better when an unknown admirer of Bobby's (one of the many he had in the city) paid to have a comfortable kennel built for him.

Visitors to Greyfriars often tried to guess what Bobby did all day. Well, for the most part, of course, he was watching his master's grave. But every day too he went to Traill's for lunch, and he also had a whole list of duties which he carried out as part of his self-appointed job of watchdog to the church and its attached cemetery. Many were the schoolboys who climbed over the wall for some game or other, only to be chased away again by the indignant terrier—sometimes minus the seat of their trousers.

Bobby lived in this fashion for nine years, and then something happened which not only put him in danger, but also threatened to get Mr. Traill into trouble too.

In Scotland, as in England and many other countries, dogs have to have a licence. Bobby, of course, had none. For years everyone had ignored this fact, but then a new campaign began in Edinburgh to enforce the dog licence law vigorously. The city's dog-catcher decided to make an example of the wretched little terrier whom everybody fussed over so much. Bobby was arrested, hauled before the magistrates, and charged with being a "vagrant dog".

There were three magistrates, and if that wasn't a bad enough ordeal for any dog, the public gallery was crammed to bursting with visitors who had come to see how he would get on. Mr. Traill was also due to appear in court: for if Bobby's crime was being a vagrant without a licence, Traill's was "harbouring" the law-breaker by giving him his lunch every day!

The watchers in the public gallery were not disappointed: after hearing all the evidence, the magistrates gravely decided to let Bobby and Mr. Traill off. But the strange affair had an even stranger sequel.

In the middle of the hearing the Lord Provost of Edinburgh (who in cities outside Scotland, would be called the Lord Mayor) happened to enter the court. His name was William Chambers, and he was so fascinated by the story that he publicly volunteered to pay for Bobby's licence himself! He also had a special collar made for the dog, to stop him ever getting into trouble again. It bore a brass plate saying: "Greyfriars Bobby, from the Lord Provost, 1867, Licensed", and from then until the end of Bobby's life, William Chambers paid Bobby's dog licence fee every year.

Nor was William Chambers the only friend Bobby had. There was Traill, of course, Bobby's first benefactor, and also sergeant Scott of the artillery. The sergeant was stationed in Edinburgh castle and, as well as visiting Bobby all the time, he used to supplement the terrier's diet by weekly gifts of steak. People now came from all over Edinburgh and Scotland—indeed from all over the world—to see Bobby: he was one of the "sights" of the city.

Bobby lived on to a very ripe old age for a dog, dying in 1872. Then—as was only fitting—he too was buried in Greyfriars, in a flower-bed close to the grave of his beloved master. The grave can still be seen, as can his collar in the city museum. But Bobby has another memorial even better known.

Shortly after his death, a granite fountain was built in his memory in Edinburgh. On top of the fountain is a bronze sculpture of the little Skye terrier himself, a terrier who, though small and not nearly as heroic as many of the great dogs of history, nonetheless managed to become one of the most famous animals of any kind who ever lived.

The clever coyote and the cleverer dove

The coyote is the wild dog of the American west and of Mexico, and everywhere he is looked upon as the cleverest dog of all. Old Man Coyote as they call him in Texas, or El Señor Coyote, which is his Mexican name, is credited with all sorts of magical tricks. But even he doesn't win every time. This is an old story from the border country between Texas and Mexico which tells how, for once, El Señor Coyote was outsmarted.

One day, El Señor Coyote was walking through the woods. He was in a good mood and feeling just a little bit hungry. Suddenly he heard a sound that made his eyes light up. It was the song of a dove, and it came from the branches of a big tree.

"Aha, that will be the excellent Señora Dove, singing a little lullaby to her babies," said Señor Coyote to himself, skipping quickly through the undergrowth until he stood at the foot of the tree.

"Hullo up there, Señora Dove," he shouted. "I couldn't help hearing your song! May I say that it does credit to our forest - charming, my dear madame, absolutely charming!"

Señora Dove was overwhelmed. She was really rather a simple soul, and flattery like this was too much for her.

"Oh, Señor Coyote, what a thing to say," she simpered. "It's just an ordinary lullaby for my babies you know."

"Ah no, I didn't know," lied Señor Coyote. "Babies you say. How very charming. I know you must be a wonderful mother."

"Well . . ." began the poor dove.

"Or at least, you would be if only . . ." said the coyote.

"If only? If only what?" asked Señora Dove, suddenly anxious to find out what was preventing her from being a good mother to her darling little chicks.

"Well, I know how busy you mothers are, really I do," said Señor Coyote. "How many chicks have you got?"

"Three," replied the dove.

"*Three?*" exclaimed the coyote, raising his eybrows. "Well, my goodness, that's surely far too many you can't possibly look after three babies properly."

"Oh, I manage, you know," said the dove.

"Impossible not properly," answered the wily coyote. "Come, I'll tell you what I'll do. I'll take one of your babies off your hands now how's that?"

"No, no, no," screamed Señora Dove.

"But yes," replied the coyote. "Just one. The ugliest one. There's no harm in that."

"There is no ugly one—they're all beautiful," said poor Señora Dove, beginning to cry pitifully.

"Never mind. One is mine! Otherwise I'll knock this tree down and get the whole lot."

When she heard this the dove was very, very frightened. Of course, she knew that the tree was tall and thick, and if a lion or bear had made the same threat as the coyote she would have laughed at him. But it didn't do to underestimate El Señor Coyote's powers. He was a devilish sort of fellow: he could do impossible things.

So poor Señora Dove took one of the sweet little fluffy baby doves in her beak and dropped it over the edge of the nest to Señor Coyote, who sat waiting below, his mouth open.

There was a short pause, then the coyote's wicked voice drifted up to the nest again.

"Now I'll have a second!" he shouted.

"You will not!" screamed the poor dove.

"Won't I though? We'll see about that," scoffed the wicked coyote. "It looks as if I'll have to knock this tree down after all."

Whereupon he began to race round and round the tree, faster and faster, until Señora Dove watching from above was so dizzy that she began to feel as though the tree was really going to fall. In desperation she threw out her second chick.

Once again there was a short pause, and then again Señor Coyote cried up at the nest.

"Now I think I'll have the last!"

"Over my dead body, you wicked animal," screeched the dove. "I don't care if the tree does fall—I'll throw no more chicks of mine to you, you monster!"

El Señor Coyote laughed. He saw that he had gone as far as he could with the dove, so with a laugh, a flick of his tail and a flash of his yellow eyes, he was off.

Poor Señora Dove! She had been so young, so innocent. This had been her first nest!

But she had learned her lesson! What's more, she determined that her one remaining chick would learn the same lesson, and so she brought it up very, very carefully indeed.

It was a female chick, and Señora Dove would often tell her: "Listen, one day you will have a nest of your own. When that time comes, never listen to that wicked Señor Coyote. Watch out for him. Avoid him. And never bargain with him—or with any other unprincipled trickster!"

Quickly the little chick grew up into a beautiful white dove; and soon she too had a nest and family of her own to look after.

She built her nest in a tree behind a farm, on the edge of a wide, dry valley.

She made friends too: with the farmer, who liked to listen to her gentle voice cooing over her little babies; with the farm animals, who were always ready for a chat; and—above all—with the two farm dogs, Villa and Zapata. They were fierce dogs of an ancient breed, white with red-brown spots, with strong teeth and loud, threatening barks.

Now the farmer noticed the firm friendship between his two mighty dogs and the tiny little dove, and he made good use of it. Whenever he wanted to call the two dogs he would simply imitate the dove's voice—whereupon Villa and Zapata would come running like two arrows from a bow.

That spring, the little dove had seven babies in her nest. Then one day, who should come through the woods but that same evil Señor Coyote who had so cruelly deceived her mother.

"Ah, Señora Dove," he said smoothly, "I hear you have the most wonderful nestful of little baby doves in the whole of Texas."

"Is that so? Well, well." answered the dove.

"Yes. How many exactly do you have?" whispered the coyote.

"Seven: four boys and three girls."

"*Seven*! Heavens, you'll never cope with so many. Better you give me one than neglect them all. You wouldn't want that, would you?" said Señor Coyote deftly.

"I'll tell you what I don't want," cried the dove. "I don't want anything to do with you! Go away."

"You had better give me the one I ask for," threatened the coyote. "For if you don't I'll just have to knock the tree down!"

"Go on then—have a try, and good luck!" squawked the dove; and she turned contemptuously back to her nest.

The great El Señor Coyote was amazed—in fact he could barely believe his own ears. For the first, the very first time in his life, he was utterly lost for words.

But little Señora Dove was not.

"Oh yes, there's another thing," she said. "I believe it's lunch time—for the dogs on the farm I mean. I'll just call them. They might fancy a bite of coyote for a change!"

Well, being amazed at the dove's opposition was one thing, but Señor Coyote wasn't going to fall for that old trick.

"A likely story!" he thought. "Call the dogs indeed!"

He heard Señora Dove calling, of course, but thinking that was all part of the trick he took no notice. He intended to race around the tree: whatever Señora Dove said, if he could only make her dizzy he would still have a chick or two.

So it was that the coyote was too busy to hear the crackling in the undergrowth, and the first he knew of the dogs' approach was when they burst through the trees and flung themselves at him with a great howl.

"Whoops! I'm off," he shouted, and raced off as fast as he could across the valley.

Never had he run so fast in all his life! Over rocks he leaped, around boulders, under low mesquite limbs, between the cactuses. But no matter how hard he ran or how cleverly he dodged, the two dogs stayed close behind him. Then, bit by bit, they began to catch him up.

"It's no good—two can always run faster than one," thought the coyote. "I'm done for. No, what's that I can see ahead?"

It looked like a small cave—it *was* a small cave. If he could only get there, Señor Coyote thought, he would be safe.

But the dogs were now so close he could hear their breathing. Would he ever make it?

YES! With a last desperate bound the coyote dived into the cave, just as the teeth of the two pursuing dogs snapped down on the last few hairs of his tail. The dogs were too big to follow him.

"Made it, made it, stupid old dogs!" Señor Coyote taunted.

Then he sat down to wait. He knew the dogs would still be waiting outside. He waited there a long time, so long that he began talking to himself, and in particular to various parts of his body.

"Ah feet, my feet. What did you do in the great chase?" he asked.

"We ran like the wind and kicked dust in the dogs' faces," said Señor Coyote on behalf of his feet.

"Now, ears, what about you?"

"We listened. One listened to the right, one to the left. We helped save you," said the ears.

"Good, good. Now eyes—what did you do?"

"Why, we saw the cave for you. We spotted the cactuses and the rocks—without us you would have been caught."

"True. Now what of you, friend tail?"

"I—well, I waved from side to side so those dogs could follow you better!"

"You did what?" bellowed Señor Coyote. "Betray me would you? Get out of this cave! Out I say! Leave at once!"

Now would you believe it? Clever El Señor Coyote then began backing out of the cave, thrusting his tail through the entrance behind him!

Outside the two dogs were patiently waiting. They got the tail, of course, and they got El Señor Coyote too. Señora Dove and her seven babies were safe at last.

Frau Moekel's thinking dog

Mannheim, where the Rhine and its tributary the Neckar meet, is the setting for the story of a dog who would probably be better known outside Germany but for the fact that most of the events that made him famous occurred during the First World War when little domestic German news ever reached the outside world.

Stories of performing and "talking" animals are not uncommon—many circuses include a talking horse among their attractions. Usually the animal responds to a series of hidden signals from his trainer and his answers follow a strict routine. All the reports about Rolf suggest that he was different. He did not learn to speak parrot-fashion, but used a code of barks to ask and answer questions. In other words, he learned to think like a human being.

Frau Moekel of Mannheim really had no idea that there was anything special about Rolf. As far as she was concerned he was just a rather nondescript stray mongrel on whom she took pity one summer day. Frau Moekel was the wife of a Mannheim solicitor, and on the spur of the moment she thought it would be a pleasant idea for her two small daughters, Frieda and Louise, to have a dog to play with. So Rolf came into their lives and was given a name and became one of the family: a quiet start to a career which would make him one of the most famous dogs in Germany.

Some weeks later, at midday, Frau Moekel was helping little Frieda with her homework. It was arithmetic, and Frieda was very bad at it. Time after time her mother went through the sum with her, explaining how it was done, using several sheets of paper, her fingers, and most of her temper to try to get her to understand. But for all her efforts it seemed to be beyond the little girl. Since the problem was nothing harder than 2 × 2 you can see just how bad Frieda was . . .

At last Frau Moekel's patience was exhausted.

"You stupid child," she burst out, shaking her daughter by the shoulder.

As she did, Frau Moekel noticed Rolf, who was sitting quietly in the corner of the room, giving her a very hard doggy stare indeed. Dogs, as is well known, detest seeing anyone under their protection punished in even the smallest way, and no people are more protected by any dog than the children of the family.

But that wasn't the kind of stare Rolf was giving her.

"He looks as if he knows the answer," Frau Moekel thought suddenly. "Come here Rolf."

Rolf came, and sat by his mistress's side.

"What do you want, Rolf?" she said. "Do

12345
5+5=

you know what 2 × 2 make? What is it?"

At that Rolf pricked up his ears, and without any hesitation whatever patted her arm exactly four times! No one has ever been more surprised than Frau Moekel.

She tried him with 5 + 5, and he got that right too! Obviously this was no ordinary dog.

That evening, Rolf had a long arithmetic exam. He passed in triumph, adding, subtracting and multiplying correctly

What next? Well, soon after, Frau Moekel decided to put the question of his future education to Rolf himself.

"Rolf, do you want to learn to speak?" she asked.

There could be no doubt from Rolf's excited leap and lively bark that the answer to that was "Yes!"

"Very well," said Frau Moekel. "I'll tell you the letters of the alphabet and you must tell me what number of barks you want to stand for each letter. Let's start with A. Rolf, how many barks shall mean A?"

Rolf thought for a moment, then barked four times.

"Right. Now B, how many for B?"

This time Rolf barked seven times.

So the lessons began, and when next day Frau Moekel checked to see if Rolf remembered what he had learned in his first lesson, she found he did. From then on she taught him five new letters every day.

Very soon Rolf had learned the entire alphabet, with the exception of the letters Q, X and V, which Frau Moekel had left out as being unnecessary. The next step was to begin teaching Rolf how to put the letters of the alphabet together to form words. Rolf seemed to enjoy every minute of it.

People soon began to find out about Rolf's remarkable abilities. One day there were a number of guests at the Moekel house. Frau Moekel was busy entertaining people with an account of her brilliant dog.

"He's very good at counting, you say?" said one smart young man. "Well then, let's see just *how* good. Ask him to count the flowers in this bouquet."

The first step of course was for the people doing the testing to know how many flowers there were themselves, so everyone in the room counted them separately. Not surprisingly, everyone arrived at a different answer. Some said there were sixteen, others fifteen, many eighteen.

Would Rolf do as well? The test would show!

"Rolf, look, we want you to count the flowers in this bouquet and tell us how many there are—go on," said Frau Moekel.

Rolf gave the flowers a long look, sniffing at them as he did so, then he barked out, "Fourteen".

Fourteen?

Never! Eighteen perhaps, or even sixteen. But fourteen was clearly ridiculous.

"Are you sure?" someone said.

Then Rolf began to make a speech, questioning his questioners.

"How many bunches of lilac are there?" he asked. "There is one."

So the bouquet was undone, and Frau Moekel counted the lilacs. There was indeed one, as Rolf had said.

"How many yellow flowers are there?" asked Rolf again. "There are four."

Four it was.

"How many blue flowers are there?" asked Rolf. "There are nine."

Sure enough there were nine—and so Rolf was proved correct: for 1 + 4 + 9 make fourteen!

After that there was an uninterrupted stream of callers at Frau Moekel's house, all anxious to ask Rolf questions.

For example, there was a Dr. Mackenzie of Genoa who asked Rolf what autumn was, and got the answer: "It is the time of apples."

Then there was Madame de Scheiwerbath who wanted to know what she could do to please Rolf. (Rather a foolish, not to mention a dangerous, question you might think.) She was told: "Wag your tail," which was the kind of answer she deserved.

Even ruder was Signor Morandetti who worked for an Italian newspaper. He apparently wasn't satisfied with Rolf's achievements in arithmetic and asked the poor dog if he would do square roots as well. "Do them yourself!" said Rolf firmly; and when it was pointed out that the journalist had come all the way from Berlin to see him, Rolf snapped, "He can go back to Berlin!"

Now, all these tests were very impressive, but to keen scientific minds they left a lot of annoying gaps. Doctors and scientists insisted on proper scientific tests being carried out.

So the tests began, but unlike the friendly little parties they were rather serious examinations, and Rolf didn't enjoy them at all. He disliked them so much that he constantly tried to hide when he knew he was in for another.

Take the first one for example.

This took the form of showing Rolf a card on which was drawn a picture of four mice nibbling a piece of cheese. Asked what he had seen, Rolf replied, "Four mice stealing cheese or bacon."

In another test Rolf was shown a toy road-direction sign with incomplete names on it: on one side was the word "Brgzabern", and on the other "Annheim". Rolf was then asked to read the inscription. This was just too easy for the little dog. He saw at once that there was a letter missing from each word. "Brgzabern" was, of course, *Bergzabern,* he barked. As for the second word, Rolf recognized the name of his home town of Mannheim instantly, and observed while barking out the letters that the bells of the town were ringing—which, indeed, at the time they were.

So the tests went on, as the professors tried to get more and more clever and make things more and more difficult for the dog—or, as they said, to make it more and more unlikely that Frau Moekel was cheating in some fashion or that Rolf was just being exceptionally lucky with his answers.

Some went too far—Professor Ziegler, for example. He was allowed to take Rolf into the kitchen alone, whereupon he unwrapped a cardboard box he was carrying and out jumped a real live rat. It didn't stay alive for very long (Rolf saw to that), but afterwards Rolf refused to do much "talking", on account of "that nasty little rat" and "that stupid Ziegler," as he put it.

Finally, a group of scientists collaborated with a local solicitor to devise the greatest test of all.

It involved four people, plus Professor Ziegler again and the solicitor, three locked rooms and three different cardboard boxes well wrapped up in brown paper.

Inside the first box was a grey soldier doll and several honey cakes. Rolf was allowed to eat the cakes. Later Frau Moekel asked him what he'd seen.

"Good cakes," he said, "and a little stump of a man."

Then the second of the boxes was taken from the locked cupboard where it had been kept, and opened. Once again there were cakes inside, which Rolf ate (presumably they were there to put him in a good mood), together with a yellow toy duck with striped wings. Rolf had no trouble with that one, even pointing out that the toy rustled in the little basket it was in inside the box.

Finally, the third box was opened. This contained nothing but food: a chop, a pork bone, and more honey cakes.

"Good, good. Go away. I'm tired!" commented Rolf, anxious to be done with the whole affair.

"But how many objects were there?" asked Professor Ziegler.

"Nineteen!" snapped Rolf.

"Nineteen . . ." smiled the Professor. He'd caught Rolf out at last. Then the smile froze on his lips. He had forgotten to count the honey cakes!

So no one will ever know whether Rolf was right or not.

Blaze, the dog from the far north

In the early spring of 1929, when the ice on the rivers had just broken up, George Barton—trapper, hunter and mining surveyor—packed up his few belongings and travelled north. The last mail had brought him a letter from his old friend and fellow trapper, Joe Le Blanc, inviting him to go and pass the summer with him.

Le Blanc had a tiny cabin in the heart of the vast pine and spruce forests of Northern Ontario, Canada: a land where even in summer a trapper could reap a rich harvest of furs and animal pelts.

The cabin lay up against a high granite ridge which sheltered it from the force of the north wind. When George and Le Blanc had finished their first meal together, and were leaning back in their big, comfortable chairs smoking their pipes, they fell to discussing the news that George had brought with him. Today, of course, a man like Le Blanc would almost certainly have a radio, but in 1929 there weren't very many of those about, and Le Blanc had to rely on the gossip of strangers, and perhaps a letter or newspaper in the post, every month or so.

At last there was a pause in the conversation and Le Blanc, taking the pipe from his mouth, said:

"By the way, Old Ottertail has a couple of huskies to sell. Good dogs they are, too. I've seen them. Good sledge dogs I'd say."

Le Blanc usually wasn't very lavish with praise, so George paid close attention to his words; in any case, he was on the lookout for a new dog. So he made up his mind there and then to look further into the matter.

"Right, I'll go and see the old fellow as soon as the lakes are free of ice," George said.

Then the two men got back to the serious business of exchanging stories, talking about old times, and catching up on all the conversation they had missed over the past couple of years.

"Old Ottertail" was a pure-blooded Ojibwa Indian (you may have heard of them under the name of Chippewa); he was a chief and the direct descendant of a long line of chiefs. The Ojibwa were now few in number—but they were proud, for their ancestors had roamed the great forest country for long ages before the first white men ever came to the land. In their great days they had fought and utterly defeated the mighty Sioux nation—"who later became so famous", as Old Ottertail would always say, with a dry laugh.

The journey to Old Ottertail's camp took two days, by canoe and on foot. But at last the old Indian and George Barton sat facing each other across the fire, talking about hunting and dogs, and dogs and hunting until, as dusk fell, the stillness of the forest was broken by a low howl.

Two young dogs came loping into view, back from a carefree afternoon spent on a private hunting expedition of their own. Both were typical cross-bred huskies: shaggy-coated and powerfully built, their mother a labrador and their father an alsatian.

In the morning George bought one from Old Ottertail. He chose the dog who seemed to take to him most, and called him Blaze, after the forest wanderer's habit of cutting or "blazing" a trail on the barks of trees as he went along.

George and Blaze went back to Le Blanc's cabin where, during the course of the summer, Blaze grew up into a magnificent animal, standing over three feet high and weighing nearly a hundred pounds.

All that summer George trained Blaze: teaching him to obey commands, to come to him when he whistled, to walk to heel, to pull a light sledge without getting the traces tangled, and to endure long hours of weary tramping through the snow. This meant going with the dog above the snowline, so George spent many days away from even the limited comfort of the cabin. If it was in the interests of Blaze's education, it was all worthwhile.

But soon the short northern summer began to wane towards autumn. The wild geese wrote the changing season across the sky, and Le Blanc began to prepare for the busy winter trapping season ahead. There would be no need to go in search of snow then.

One day, after the first snowfalls had already started, George decided to make a quick trip in search of a new beaver meadow he had heard other trappers talking about in the summer.

Le Blanc was worried. "George, old friend," he said, "you have left it too late. Don't go now. A bad blizzard could come at any moment."

"Don't worry about me," replied George with a laugh. "I'll be back in just a few days' time."

"Maybe, maybe. But I warn you, stay as short a time as you can on the shores of Elbow Lake—that's a bad place to be caught in the open."

So George and Blaze set out. They went quickly, with Blaze romping on ahead until George's sharp whistle brought him back again. Then he would leap up at his master, giving a sort of husky grin, as if to say, "See what a good time I'm having!" Now and again he would almost stir up trouble by barking furiously at a passing bear or moose. But a sharp "Come here, Blaze!" always brought him to heel.

Together they swung gaily along the trail. The clear frosty air set the blood tingling in their veins, and the only sounds to be heard were the "twang twang" of George's snowshoes, and the occasional distant bark of a fox or a wolf's howl. George found no trace of beaver.

On the afternoon of the fourth day out from Le Blanc's cabin, when they were already heading back, the first signs of trouble appeared; the wind began to gust strongly from the north, while great grey snow clouds started to build up. Then, as Blaze and George hurried along the homeward trail, they heard the low moan of the approaching blizzard.

The trail ran for part of the way along a saw-backed ridge, then passed into a deep pine wood. Here the thick branches, already heavily laden with snow, completely hid the sky from view, and every so often an eddying gust of wind sent a miniature avalanche tumbling down.

Suddenly George heard a wild piercing scream just behind him. Before he could turn, a crushing blow struck his shoulders sending him sprawling headlong in the snow, while some unseen creature clawed fiercely at his back.

For a moment George was dazed and confused. Then his mind cleared: he realized that whatever had been on his back was there no longer, and that a tremendous battle was going on close by him.

At first George could barely distinguish one contestant from another; but when they drew apart for a moment, George saw that his gallant young Blaze was struggling with a full-grown lynx. The animal must have leapt from a tree on to George's back. Blaze had come immediately to his master's rescue.

Quickly George whipped out his black-handled revolver and, resting the barrel against the crook of his left arm, tried to take aim.

"Hold still, hold still," he muttered.

But it was no good: the two animals were locked in combat again, and it was impossible to take proper aim. Great patches of crimson began to appear in the snow as the blood of dog and lynx flowed freely.

Then, at last, Blaze rolled on top of the lynx and, with a supreme effort, sank his fangs into its throat. Both animals fell back: the lynx dead, and poor Blaze totally exhausted. He was bleeding heavily from a deep claw mark down the side of his face.

"Poor fellow, poor fellow," said George softly, and bandaged the wound as best as he could. "Now we must be getting home—the blizzard is even more dangerous than the lynx!"

For a time, however, Blaze was too weak to stand; there was nothing for it but to wait until he had recovered sufficiently to go on. So they waited. Waited while the blizzard fairly screamed through the trees; waited with their heads bowed against cold, wind and snow; waited while great branches—and whole trees—snapped off like dry twigs under the force of the wind and their burden of snow.

At the end of an hour Blaze was able to walk, and slowly the two of them fought their way homeward. George was in constant fear of their being crushed by a falling branch, or of poor Blaze not having sufficient strength, or of their missing the trail and getting lost.

At last, through the swirling snowflakes, George saw the winking light from the window of Le Blanc's cabin. At that precise moment, Blaze's strength finally gave out, and he collapsed in the snow. Despite the encouraging words and help of his master, he simply could not get up again.

Somehow George got Blaze on to his back and struggled with him to the cabin, where he burst in on his anxious friend.

It took weeks of devoted nursing to restore Blaze to health, but at last he fully recovered—apart from a scar on his muzzle where the lynx's fierce claws had gouged a mark that would never disappear.

For several seasons George and Blaze hunted among the forests and lakes, but then George moved to the town of Hamilton, 800 miles to the south.

Blaze never really settled down in the town. His happiest moments were at Christmas time, when the sight and smell of the Christmas tree reminded him of the pine forests of his homeland. As time passed, George also tired of the city life. Then, for years at a time, man and dog would return to Joe Le Blanc's cabin among the tall trees under the northern stars.

The lean dog and the hungry wolf

The French writer La Fontaine lived from 1621 to 1695. His fables were chiefly based on the much earlier writing of Aesop, and were written in verse. They are all about animals, and several of them are about dogs. La Fontaine's aim was to show animals thinking, feeling and acting like human beings, and in this way to make comments on the way people behave.

Once, a fine brown spaniel called Tray went for his usual morning walk in the forest near his home. Tray wasn't the most adventurous of dogs and he seldom went very far from home or from the paths he knew. But, as luck would have it, on this particular day he wandered further afield and even chased a rabbit—which was certainly very unusual for him. Tray got himself completely lost. Being a sensible sort of animal though, this didn't upset him as much as it might you or me. Instead, he began to cast around for some sight or scent he could recognize.

Tray wasn't the only animal looking for something in the forest that day. Slink, the wolf, was there too, and he was hungry.

After a time Slink came to a glade in the forest; he sniffed about, found nothing, and was on the point of moving on when he heard a movement in the trees and Tray came in sight. Now Tray had rich, silky brown hair and big, soft brown eyes. He was really a most handsome spaniel. But the wolf didn't think of him like that at all.

"Dear me," Slink thought, "here's a surprise! Hmm, a dog! No finer meat than dog, I say."

With a bound, he leaped out in front of Tray.

"What d-do you w-want with m-m-me?" stammered the poor spaniel.

"Simple, my dear tasty little fellow," replied the wolf. "I want to eat you!"

The wolf's great jaws opened, and Tray could see rows of long, sharp teeth.

Now, Tray was no fool. Spaniels never are, and what he lacked in sheer size and strength he more than made up for in intelligence. Thoughtfully he looked the wolf up and down.

"Eat me? Ho, Ho! Well, times must be really bad in the forest! What is it? Gamekeepers getting too clever for you? Hen coops too strongly built?"

"Times getting bad? What on earth do you mean?" laughed Slink, just a little uneasily. "Stop wasting my time. I want to get on with my meal."

"Oh yes, of course," said Tray. "You want to get on with eating me. Well, as I

said, you must be going through a bad patch. I mean, eating *me*! Why, my dear wolf, just look at me closely. I'm all skin and bone. Nothing to chew on at all. Hardly enough to give you indigestion."

"Hmm, you don't look too bad to me," said Slink.

"Oh, don't let this long hair of mine deceive you," answered Tray. "Hair makes a poor dinner. See how you can count every one of my ribs. Look how drawn my face is. Look how thin my legs are."

"Well, maybe you aren't quite in the best condition," answered Slink, "but if I don't eat you now I may never get another chance."

"Ah, but there you are wrong," replied Tray smoothly, for he could see that he was beginning to get the better of the wolf in the argument. "You see, at the moment I've been lost for two or three days. That's why I'm so thin." (Of course, Tray had only been lost for *one* day—but the wolf didn't know that.) "At home I eat very well," the spaniel went on. "Why it's three, four, even five meals a day in my house. And next month it's going to be better than ever."

"What's so special about next month?" the wolf asked.

"A wedding, that's what's special. My lord is throwing an enormous party to celebrate the marriage of his only daughter. Everyone from miles around will be there, and I'll get my fill a dozen times over. So if you really want to eat me it would be far better if you did it *after* the wedding than before it. Come in the evening—I'll be as fat as butter then . . ."

"As fat as butter, eh?" said Slink. "Well, perhaps there's some sense in what you say after all. But how can I be certain that you'll keep your word?"

"I'll give my word of honour, of course," said Tray. "But in any case, you are so much bigger and stronger than I am that you could come and get me whenever you wanted. You are so powerful!"

"Why, so I am, so I am," said Slink smiling—for wolves are better at hunting than thinking.

So, believe it or not, the wolf let Tray go: indeed, he did more. He actually helped the spaniel find his way home again, for the wolf now looked on Tray as a kind of investment: to be looked after and cherished until it was time to cash him in—in other words, until it was time to eat him.

Everyone was overjoyed to see Tray when he limped sadly through the great stone gateway of the house where he lived. He whined piteously, of course, just to make everyone sorry for him; and soon he was the centre of an admiring and sympathetic crowd.

There was his master—he was glad to see Tray back:

"Tray, my dear fellow, what happened, eh?" he said. "Did you lose yourself? Poor old boy. Poor old boy," and so on.

There was the mistress of the house:

"Oh Tray, I was so worried," she squeaked. "I thought someone had run off with you. What would I do without you? Come, eat a peach. Eat two peaches!"

But the most delighted of them all was their daughter, the girl who was going to be married:

"Tray, Tray, Tray, thank goodness you've come back!" she said, stroking his head. "If you hadn't it would have ruined my wedding completely—indeed I don't think there would have been a wedding at all. Now, you shall sit on my lap during supper; you shall eat from my plate, and you shall have a dish of wine all for yourself."

So it went on. But there was someone else who was overjoyed to see Tray back again—so overjoyed that he leaped in the air with pleasure, howled with delight, bounded to and fro, and nearly broke his chain with excitement. This was Tray's special friend, Gripper: Gripper the watch-dog, Gripper the doorkeeper, Gripper the enormous dobermann pinscher.

They looked strange side by side, the small brown spaniel and the gigantic black dobermann—who was as tall as a man from the ground and as long as a man along it—but friends they were, the greatest of friends. Indeed, Tray hadn't been telling all that much of a lie when he said there was limitless food at his house. Only he left out the fact that he gave about half of everything he got to Gripper. For, as is often the case, Tray's fond master and mistress gave Tray, their pet, twice as much as was good for him; while Gripper, their watchdog, got only half as much as he really needed. This was supposed to make him fiercer.

Gripper wasn't kept chained up all the time, of course. Sometimes he was given the day off, and every evening, like Tray, he had a walk. The two dogs went together. Often they had mock battles with each other: Tray would leap over the dobermann while the great animal rolled on the ground; or he would run between the dobermann's legs and butt him in the tummy, while Gripper tried to give Tray playful punches with his enormous long legs, or to pick him up (neatly and gently) in his mouth and roll him over.

Naturally Gripper was very anxious to hear all about Tray's adventures.

"What happened, old fellow? How did you lose yourself?" he asked kindly.

"I was so silly. I chased a rabbit and got lost—more lost than I've ever been," Tray said. "It took me a whole day to find my way back."

"Poor little Tray; you should be more careful," said the dobermann. "You are far too reckless."

"Reckless? Well, perhaps," Tray said quietly. "But if I hadn't thought pretty quickly I would have ended up as a snack for a wolf."

"You would have ended up as what? A snack? For a wolf?" bellowed Gripper, and he stood on his hind legs and pawed at the air furiously. Gripper detested wolves.

"You may get a chance to meet this one. In fact, I'm sure you will," said Tray, beginning to chuckle. "Let me tell you the whole story from the beginning."

A month later, the day for the daughter of the house's wedding arrived. The great banquet was everything Tray said it would be; and he ate and ate to his heart's content.

Later that evening, when the guests were all inside the house dancing and talking, Tray slipped away from the party and, giving a wink to Gripper—who sat thoughtfully just out of sight behind the gate—he went and stood a pace or two out in the road in front of the house.

"He'll be coming any minute now, I expect," Tray said. "Be ready!"

Sure enough, as the sun was about to disappear below the horizon, a long, dark, evil shape came gliding down the road towards the house from the direction of the forest. It was Slink.

"Hello," said Tray cheerfully. "I've been waiting. I'm ready!"

"Good! Good! I'm ready too," drooled Slink. "I've been looking forward to this for a month; I can see you've fed well since I saw you in the forest. No skin and bone now! My word, you really are as fat as butter! Now come with me to the forest—where I can eat you in peace and comfort."

"Just hang on a moment, will you?" Tray asked.

"Hang on? What for?" replied Slink.

"For the gatekeeper," said Tray. "He's coming too!"

Then, before the wolf could say another word, Gripper gave a roar and a leap and shot out from where he had been hiding.

"Aho! Help! Aaaah!" howled the wolf as Gripper grabbed him by the neck. "Forget it—and my compliments to your gatekeeper!"

Then he turned tail and fled up the road faster than any wolf has ever run in the history of wolfdom—and was never seen in that district again.

Cerberus, watchdog of the Underworld

Cerberus was the name given by the ancient Greeks to the monstrous she-dog which they believed guarded the Underworld of Tartarus—the land under the earth where all people went after they died.

There never was, nor ever will be, a stranger dog than Cerberus. For she was thought to have at least three heads—some people said fifty! One was an ordinary dog's head, another the head of a horse, and the third the head of a lion.

As if that wasn't enough, Cerberus's hair was made up of hissing, live, poisonous snakes; and her tail was like that of some horrible stinging insect.

A fierce animal for a grim job: for Cerberus it was who guarded the bank of the river Styx—the western boundary of the ghost-filled Underworld.

One part of Tartarus, the Asphodel Fields, was a dark, cheerless place where the souls of the dead were like twittering bats. Here Hades and Persephone ruled as king and queen. Another part was more horrible still. This was the punishment fields where the ghosts of the wicked, or of those who had simply offended the gods in some way, were tortured by Hades or his servants.

Other parts of the Underworld were better and were not ruled over by Hades and Persephone at all, but by Cronus—a far older god than Hades, though not older than Persephone, who had been queen of the Underworld before Hades became king.

The first of these other areas was Elysium. Elysium was a happy land of perpetual day, without cold or snow, where the souls of those who had lived perfect lives entertained themselves with games and music and parties without end. They could choose to be reborn on earth whenever they pleased, though if they did they had to live another perfect life before they could return to Elysium. And for the very special people who had lived three separate, perfect, earthly lives and three times gone to Elysium, there was a separate place to live—the Fortunate Isles. There they stayed for ever in perfect happiness, with men and women of the same quality as themselves for company.

Cerberus and the other grim servants

guarded well the gateway to the terrible domain of Hades and Persephone. Few except the dead ever entered; and even fewer—dead or alive—ever left. It was said that Cerberus had been there before Hades, and even before Persephone, and had once ruled Tartarus herself. If that was true it certainly explained why she was so severe a guard.

Apart from Cerberus, Hades' most important servant was Charon, the ferryman who rowed the souls of the dead across the terrifying waters of the Styx. Charon was something of a miser; and so the ancient Greeks always buried their dead with a coin under their tongues so they would be able to pay him the fare he demanded for rowing them across the river.

Of the very few living mortal heroes who ever managed to descend to Tartarus and return alive to the earth above, none was more famous than Hercules.

You have probably heard about him, and know that he was famous from childhood for his tremendous strength. Indeed, his strength was superhuman, for—according to the old Greek legends—Hercules' father was Zeus, the greatest of all the gods, though his mother was a mortal woman.

Hercules was always a great favourite of Zeus, and of some of the other gods and goddesses too, especially Athene (after whom the city of Athens was named) and Hermes. This was very fortunate for him because his life was full of the most dangerous adventures. What's more, Zeus's wife Hera hated Hercules, and was constantly scheming against him. Thanks to Zeus, Athene and Hermes, and not least to his own great courage and strength, her schemes usually came to nothing.

One of Hera's plans, however, had a terrible result. She was so jealous of Hercules' success and popularity that she caused him to go mad and, in his madness, to kill six of his own children and two of his brother's. Hera did not bring about his downfall as she had hoped, but of course Hercules had to be punished. He was forced to promise to do twelve great Labours—great, difficult, and often dangerous tasks—to atone for the dreadful thing he had done. One after the other Hercules performed every Labour, until only one remained to be done: the twelfth and last, the most difficult and the most dangerous of all.

For Hercules had to descend to the Underworld and bring away the terrible dog Cerberus to the living world—bring her away, that is, against not only her own will but against that of Hades and Persephone too.

Fortunately, Athene and Hermes stood by him in this his greatest peril. They guided him safely down through the dark, secret places of the world, and brought him, at last, safely to the banks of the river Styx.

They could go no further, however, and from this point on Hercules had to depend on his own courage and resourcefulness—which were limitless—and on the weapons and armour he had brought with him—which were formidable!

For armour he wore the skin of a lion. It was no ordinary lion's skin, however; this was the hide of the Nemean lion, which he had killed in his very first Labour, strangling it with his bare hands. The skin was proof against iron, bronze and stone.

For weapons Hercules carried a mighty club cut from the wood of the wild olive tree, and a great bow made from the two horns of a wild antelope, joined in the centre with bronze.

All in all, Hercules was the most frightening looking mortal who had ever been seen in the grim land of the dead in all its history.

So it was that old Charon took one look at him and was so terrified that he rowed him across the river without daring to ask for the usual fare. Perhaps even Cerberus herself rather preferred to keep out of Hercules' way: she never put in an appearance at this time at all. Indeed, nearly all the inhabitants of Tartarus fled away from the fierce mortal, and Hercules was able to wander around to his heart's content, doing all kinds of mischief.

Very soon Hades and Persephone in person arrived to put a stop to it.

"What do you want here?" cried Hades haughtily. "This is my kingdom and no one may enter it without my permission."

"Yet I have done so, and you have no power over me," replied Hercules, jutting out his chin and shaking his enormous club under Hades' nose in no very respectful manner.

"Be careful how you speak to me," hissed Hades. "Remember, I am a *god*, Lord of the Underworld, ruler of the dead, owner of all the treasures of gold and silver and jewels that lie buried in the earth; while you are a mortal man—a strong one perhaps—in a lion's skin!"

"I am indeed a mortal man, as you say," Hercules replied. "Strong too—yes, very strong. Perhaps stronger than you would like! Moreover, I am here with the approval of Zeus himself, greatest of all the gods; and with the help of Athene and Hermes, too!"

"Peace, good Hercules," interrupted Persephone, who was not only older but much more gracious than her husband. "I am sure so great a hero came here for some good reason—not just to disturb the peace."

"Great Persephone, it is as you say," Hercules answered. "It was my fate to commit a terrible crime in a fit of madness, and for this I have to perform twelve great Labours. Eleven I have accomplished. Now, for the twelfth I have come here to take your servant Cerberus back to the world of the living: though once she is there not I nor anyone else will hinder her return to your dominion!"

"Listen to this boastful fellow," scoffed Hades. "We know of your Labours well enough, but they are nothing compared with the one you are attempting now. Already your life is in great danger—yet you talk as if Cerberus will follow you out of Tartarus like an obedient dog walking at your heel. If you want Cerberus you will have to overcome her . . ."

"Indeed, I came expecting to," said Hercules, looking thoughtfully at his club.

"Ah, your club . . ." said Hades. "I am afraid I must disappoint you. I will not allow you to use either your club or your bow when you fight Cerberus. Now, go . . . and fight."

So Hercules searched for Cerberus and, having found her, threw aside his weapons and prepared to fight with his bare hands alone.

It was the greatest battle of man and beast ever seen. Cerberus lashed at Hercules with her scything claws, which were as long as swords and as sharp; she bit at him with all three of her terrible heads, whose teeth were as big as battle axes and as powerful; the poisonous snakes that clustered around her neck struck at him with venom deadlier than that of any living snake; and her wickedly barbed tail flailed at him like a spearhead.

Yet Hercules' impregnable lion skin kept him safe against all this, and all the time he strove to grip the monster's throat with his enormously powerful hands. At last he did so; then he squeezed and squeezed until she had no choice but to surrender or choke.

Hercules bound her with her own dog's chain and dragged the monstrous beast back through Hades' kingdom, back across the Styx, and back to the world beneath the sun.

So ended the last Labour of Hercules: at last the gods could forgive him.

But what of Cerberus? Well, since no trace or word of her has ever been found or heard on earth again, she must have found her way home to Tartarus.

So even she behaved as a good dog should, at the last.

The phantom rustler

The little courtroom of Lyttelton, South Island, New Zealand, was crowded almost to the rafters. It was the most sensational trial ever to be held there, and people had come from all over South Island to be present.

In the dock stood John McKenzie: gaunt, lean, muscular, red-haired; born in Ross-shire in the highlands of Scotland, many thousands of miles away.

John was on trial for rustling or stealing sheep, and the prosecution hoped by his conviction to end two years of uninterrupted, and hitherto utterly inexplicable thefts. In those two years John McKenzie had joined in hunting for the thief as resolutely as any man, but now he stood accused of committing the crimes himself. Yet where was the evidence?

"There's no man can say they saw me take a single sheep," John muttered.

Indeed, no man could. For it was a strange case—sheep vanishing in the night, seemingly into thin air. Many had said it was the work of a ghost, a Phantom Rustler. Who else could make sheep, of all creatures, travel by night? And what happened to the sheep afterwards? No trace of any of them was ever found.

Yet here stood the wiry figure of John McKenzie—an unghostlike figure if ever there was one—though the evidence against him seemed thin enough. True, stolen sheep were thought to have passed through the valley where he lived: they could easily have strayed there. True, John had dealings with people who went to the market of Otago in the next province, where it was known some of the stolen sheep had been sold: there was no crime in talking to people from Otago—many of those in the courtroom went there often enough.

No, there was not nearly enough evidence! Then the prosecution played its trump card: they produced the Phantom Rustler. But it was no ghost that entered the court, though it wasn't a man or a woman, either.

It was a dog: Kelpie, John McKenzie's Scotch collie. With an excited yelp she struggled and tugged to reach her master, and when the constable released her she raced to where John stood in the dock and leapt at him, tugging at his sleeves, licking his hands and face, pawing at his chest. There could be no mistaking the warmth of the reunion.

"Oh, lass, lass. You have surely betrayed

me now!" sighed John, holding the dog's head in his hands and rubbing her ears. "I'm as good as sentenced already!"

For John it was the end of a story which had begun thousands of miles away in the Scottish highlands where he was born. John was one of the settlers who, in the early years of the nineteenth century, left their homes in Europe to seek better things in the new colonies.

He went first to Australia; then in 1847 moved on once more, to South Island, New Zealand.

One of the first things he did there was to buy a black collie with tan-coloured muzzle and feet. He named her Kelpie, and took her with him when he went exploring. There was plenty of free open land in New Zealand, but land in itself meant very little. John needed sheep to breed and sell, but before he could get sheep he needed money. And John had no money, so if he wanted sheep he had to find some other way of getting them.

It was while he was exploring the wild country north of Otago that he began to see a possible solution. In fact there he found exactly what he was looking for. Well below the snow-line, but surrounded on all sides by the high shoulders of the mountains, he found a hidden valley. Protected from the weather and well grassed, it overlooked the famous sheep country of the Canterbury plains, and yet was hidden from people looking from the south. To the north, a narrow secret pass led out of the valley towards Otago and the next province.

"Will you look at this, lass!" exclaimed John to his dog. "Why, we shall graze a thousand sheep here, Kelpie girl, and though they don't know it, it's those fools down there on the plain who will be sending them to me. But there's plenty of work to be done first, for both of us."

So John began to train Kelpie in a way no sheepdog had ever been trained before—and to do things that no other sheepdog could do. He taught her to herd sheep entirely on her own, without any direction or instruction from him—and at night.

One day in 1853 everything was ready. Kelpie was trained, the valley was full of rich green grass, and below on the broad plains was a tempting herd of five hundred sheep belonging to a local company.

That afternoon, McKenzie and Kelpie paid the shepherd a visit.

"Good day to you, friend," said McKenzie, doing his best to master the unfamiliar English tongue. "Good day. I am McKenzie—it is a fine flock you have."

"Yes it is," answered the shepherd. "Five hundred of the best! They'll fetch a good price at market I'll wager. But I don't often have any company: sit yourself down, have a mug of tea—come, I've just brewed it."

"I will. My thanks to you," said John.

"That's a fine-looking dog you have there," the shepherd commented.

"She is that," John agreed, and whispered to Kelpie in Gaelic: "Remember the way to this sheep station. Tonight I want you to come back and take that fine flock back to the valley."

"What are you telling her?" asked the unsuspecting shepherd.

"Oh, just that she's a good girl," John lied.

Kelpie understood at once. She gave a little growl of acknowledgement, then dropped down on all fours with her chin on her paws, and took an innocent-looking sleep. She certainly didn't *look* like a sheep rustler.

An hour or two passed and at length John rose to leave.

"I must be getting back now," he said. "It's a long march to my home from here. I won't be there before nightfall."

Later that evening, however, John returned—alone—to the shepherd's hut.

"I didn't like the look of the weather," he told the shepherd, "so I turned back. May I shelter here for the night? I sent my dog home to look after my place, but then she's better protected against the wind and rain than I am. And she can travel a lot faster."

So the two men chatted on again. Then before turning in for the night the shepherd went outside to take a last look at his fine flock.

"The devil! They're gone!" he cried.

Outside, the fields were totally empty: there was not a single sheep to be seen in any direction.

Together, the shepherd and John McKenzie roused the countryside. Dozens of sheep herders and settlers joined in the search for the vanished sheep, but not a sign of them could they find. The hunt went on for days, and, in fact, just about everyone in the district was suspected of stealing them—except John McKenzie!

"It couldn't have been Scotch John," the farmers would say. "He spent the whole night with the shepherd."

In fact, of course, Kelpie had done what no one thought possible—she had moved sheep faster by night than anyone, or anything, had ever managed to move them even by day. Along the narrow, twisty, stony mountain roads she had hurried them to the valley. Then, in the morning she had hurried them out of it again: through the secret pass and away to where an accomplice of John's was waiting to sell the sheep as his own in the Otago market.

Time passed, and although the sheep farmers maintained a constant guard with mounted armed men, the rustling continued.

Then one night the watchers saw something: a flock of sheep moving in close formation towards the mountains.

"I don't believe it!" one guard whispered to another. "Sheep travelling at night, and without a shepherd—it's not possible!"

"Possible or not, let's get after them!" cried the other, and off they galloped.

But as they approached, the flock broke formation and scattered aimlessly across the hillside. When the guards rode off, the sheep once again closed up, and continued their march, one behind the other.

"It's a ghost that's driving them—it must be," said the first guard.

"Aye, a phantom!" said the other. "A Phantom Rustler. What else could drive sheep at night and then disappear into thin air?"

So it went on, for two years. Rustling after rustling, hue and cry after hue and cry, with never a trace of the sheep, and never a breath of suspicion falling on John McKenzie.

Until the day when word came from Otago of a black-and-tan collie who regularly drove flocks of sheep to the market from the south. The dog was seized, and then at last the sheepmen went to John's valley. They saw the trampled grass and the hidden pass to the north. Then John himself was arrested . . .

John McKenzie was sentenced, that day at Lyttelton, South Island, New Zealand, to five years' imprisonment, and despite his pleas he was not allowed to take Kelpie with him into confinement.

Indeed, there were some who said that Kelpie should be shot for her part in the crimes. But no: she had, after all, only obeyed her master as a good sheepdog should. In fact a group of sheepmen tried to put her to work—even finding a Gaelic-speaking shepherd for her. But Kelpie would work for no one but John, and the finest sheepdog in the history of New Zealand went into retirement. For years after, however, her puppies were eagerly bought by sheepmen from all over the country.

John, meanwhile, made such a habit of escaping from prison that it was decided to release him after he had served only a year of his sentence: that is, release him on condition he left New Zealand for ever.

John McKenzie left New Zealand in disgrace and alone, for he was not allowed to take Kelpie with him. But his name was not forgotten: the country which was the scene of his "phantom rustling" is called McKenzie country to this day.

The grave of Gelert

To the south of Mount Snowdon, in Wales, is a region of mighty hills and sharp mountain peaks, of storms and snow and mist, of tumbled stone and cliffs, heather and cold mountain streams. In this region, the villages hug the hillsides closely in the hundreds of steep valleys—one of which, the hidden valley of Gelert, contains the little village of Beddgelert.

Beddgelert is rather special, for it is named after a dog: in Welsh Beddgelert means "the grave of Gelert". This is the story of Gelert the hound, and how he came to give his name to the village and the valley.

It all took place long, long ago. In past days this part of Wales looked much the same as it does now—with snow on the mountain peaks and sheep on the hills. But whereas today it is a peaceful land where people from the cities can forget for a while the noisy, crowded streets, in those days it was often the scene of fierce and deadly fighting.

From the natural fortresses of the mountains the Welsh long maintained a desperate resistance to the English invaders, who wanted to win possession of Wales for themselves.

The Welsh held out for a long time. Again and again they would humiliate the proud English generals and kings who marched upon them with their powerful armies. Even today there are few roads in this part of Wales; then there were none at all. The Welsh soldiers would cunningly retreat into the unmapped mountains of their homeland, emerging to harass the enemy at the most difficult places along the route.

Sometimes the Welsh would simply wait for the English to exhaust themselves with marching and searching. Sometimes they would attack the English in the flanks or rear, or cut off their supplies.

But despite their efforts it was a war the Welsh could never win. With each defeat the English simply became more determined than ever to conquer, and always they had more men to pour into the fight; while as time went by the Welsh resistance grew weaker and more desperate, and their soldiers fewer and more hard-pressed.

One of the leaders of this resistance was a prince called Llewelyn, and Gelert was his hound. In the old tales Gelert is described as a greyhound, but probably he was more like what we would call an Irish wolfhound: grey in colour perhaps, but rough-coated, square-jawed, and very powerful.

Once, schoolchildren used to learn by heart a poem about Gelert. Today it is less well-known, but you will be able to read

some of its verses later in this story.

It was a bitterly cold winter's day, a day when the sky seemed about to touch the earth: and, indeed, the fat slate-coloured clouds hid the top of Snowdon and the higher hills. The rain slanted down without a pause, driven by a fierce wind. It was a day when no one went outside unless they were forced to.

Yet had you been there you would have seen, hooded and muffled to the eyes, heads bowed, a thin, straggling line of riders on shaggy-coated mountain ponies, slowly winding their way up what is now called the valley of Gelert.

They were Prince Llewelyn and all who remained of his sturdy hill fighters. Bowmen and spearmen, they had fought the English from valley to valley until, driven back by sheer weight of numbers, tired and hungry, they had sought refuge in their last place of safety—the hidden valley.

Even this valley could only shelter them for a short time. They had to find a way out through the encircling English before the valley ceased to be a refuge and became a trap. So, under cover of the terrible weather, the prince was off to reconnoitre the position of his enemies: well-provisioned and well-equipped as he knew them to be, he was certain they would not make a move on such a bad day. It was too good a chance to risk losing.

Yet there was a risk. In his desperate fighting retreat Llewelyn had been forced to bring with him his baby son, and now the prince had to leave his child behind in the best shelter the valley could provide, while he and his men searched for an escape route.

The shelter was no castle—though the poem says it was—nor a house, nor a cottage either: it was just a poor hut hidden in a cleft of rock and overhung by a cliff face. Llewelyn's men had piled rocks into rough walls, laid branches across the top and over all had stretched some old canvas, weighted with stones to stop the wind from taking it.

Inside, the baby prince was wrapped in warm blankets and skins—and he was sleeping.

But though he was left behind, he was not left alone. For by the basket that served as a cradle lay the huge, grey, silent form of Gelert, watching:

. . . a lamb at home,
A lion in the chase . . .

the bravest and most faithful servant Llewelyn had.

Away then rode the prince, tormented with doubts and the bitter memories of better days when, as the fire and candle-light shone in some great hall of carved wood and stone, he had feasted from dishes of silver while sweet-voiced bards recited ancient poems and sang and played upon the harp. Away he rode to spend a fruitless day peering through dripping thickets and across sodden hills at the camps of the English army—seeking an escape route but finding his enemies holding the valley tight, guarding every pass, watching from every hilltop.

There was great danger for Llewelyn and his men that day. But greater danger lurked behind him, in the hidden valley where he thought his child lay in safety.

For while Llewelyn and his riders picked their way through the hills, a wolf, gaunt and desperate with hunger, came prowling down. With his burning eyes he watched the riders leave. Now he crept closer, mad for the food he hoped to find in the camp.

On he came . . . he smelled the child sleeping within. He smelled the hound too, but his hunger was stronger than his caution.

"Growl . . .!" Gelert was aware of him.

For a moment the two stood facing each other, then, with terrible fierceness, they hurled themselves into the attack. The battle was long and remorseless in its savagery. The great hound and enormous wolf tore and scratched and bit and wrestled;

fur and flesh and blood spattered everywhere; the mountain shelter was battered to ruin piece by piece and stone by stone, by the battle within.

At last, with a twist and a fierce thrust of his head, faithful Gelert ripped away the throat of the murdering beast which was trying to kill the child of his master. A brooding silence, broken only by Gelert's laboured breath, returned to the camp.

But the battle had left Gelert sorely wounded. Bleeding from a dozen fearful gashes, he laid himself down where he had fought and, licking his wounds, waited for Llewelyn's return.

Llewelyn meanwhile had abandoned his mission. It had been a failure: the English were everywhere. So, tired and hopeless, he and his handful of dispirited followers made their way back to the little camp.

"At least I have my son to return to," Llewelyn thought, "and Gelert—ah, Gelert!"

But then he came in sight of the camp.

"Great heavens! What has happened here?" he cried, dismounting.

. . . Aghast the chieftain stood;
The hound all o'er was smeared with gore,
His lips, his fangs, ran blood.

Wounded as Gelert was, when he saw his master he gave a joyous bark. But then, catching the look of horror and amazement on Llewelyn's face, the dog dropped down as the prince approached, trying to lick his feet.

"Blood, blood, everywhere blood," cried Llewelyn, "but where's my son? Hell hound! What have you done with my son?"

He called his child—no voice replied—
He searched with terror wild;
Blood, blood he found on every side,
But nowhere found his child.

Suddenly Llewelyn knew what had happened. Or he thought he knew. Poor Gelert could only look up in silent appeal as the prince drew his long sword.

"*. . . My child's by thee destroyed,*"
The frantic father cried;
And to the hilt his vengeful sword
He plunged in Gelert's side.

Gelert screamed, and fell down, not dead yet, but dying. But his howls did something which all the previous noise of the fight and Llewelyn's shouting had failed to do. They awakened Llewelyn's sleeping child. Cold, hungry, and wondering sleepily what all the noise was about, he began to cry.

With mingled wonder, confusion, joy and fear, Llewelyn tore at the ruins about him. Perhaps his child was still alive?

Concealed beneath a tumbled heap
His worried hurried search had missed,
All glowing from his rosy sleep
The cherub boy he kissed.
Nor scathe had he, nor harm, nor dread
But the same couch beneath,
Lay a gaunt wolf, all torn and dead,
Tremendous still in death.

But what about Gelert?

Ah, what was then Llewelyn's pain!
For now the truth was clear;
His gallant hound the wolf had slain,
To save Llewelyn's heir.

Flinging away his sword, and blinded by his tears, Llewelyn dropped to his knees by the fallen body of Gelert. Gelert opened his eyes for one final moment: there was his dear master, the master he had loved and who yet had killed him . . . Who knows what a man would have done in Gelert's place, but Gelert with his last strength licked his master's hand.

Vain, vain was all Llewelyn's woe:
"Best of thy kind, adieu!
The frantic blow which laid thee low,
This heart shall ever rue."
And now a gallant tomb they raise,
With costly sculpture deck'd;
And marbles storied with his praise
Poor Gelert's bones protect.

Llewelyn fought on against the English. He is remembered still by his countrymen; and his faithful hound Gelert will never be forgotten while Beddgelert stands.

The prince and the three whippets

For hundreds of years the gipsy people have wandered all over Europe, and in many other parts of the world too. Whether they invented this story themselves or learned it on their travels is, therefore, difficult to say—but don't be surprised if it reminds you of many other stories you know.

In the flickering sunlight among the trees a young man was riding—riding for all he was worth. He was riding for his life! It was young Prince Merrifyl. At his birth a gipsy had foretold that when he came of age at eighteen he would be killed by the Black Dog of the Wild Forest. Now it was the afternoon of his eighteenth birthday—and the hunt was on.

Behind him came the Black Dog, four times bigger than a wolf, with eyes blazing like coals and a scarlet tongue lolling from between wicked teeth. Every minute that passed brought him closer to the fleeing young man.

Suddenly, Merrifyl caught sight of an old gipsy caravan beside the road. By it an old gipsy woman was tending a fire burning in a three-legged fire-basket.

"Hide me, hide me!" pleaded the prince.

"Quick—crawl into the ash-hole under the fire," replied the woman. Merrifyl did as he was told, burying himself among the ashes. But, just then, the Black Dog came bounding out of the trees, The people of the forest said that no one looked into his eyes and lived to tell the tale—but the old gipsy stood her ground. And that wasn't all. For she pulled a long whip from her belt and began lashing the Black Dog with it, while, at the same moment, her own dog rushed to her assistance.

Merrifyl looked on in amazement. For the gipsy woman's dog was only a little, white whippet bitch. But together, whippet and whip drove the monstrous Black Dog back

into the trees. The prince was saved! Until the morning at least!

But, as it turned out, the morning brought some comfort.

"Good-bye, Prince Merrifyl—oh yes, I know who you are without you telling me," laughed the old gipsy. "You have not escaped from the Black Dog yet, but I will help you. Take my little dog. Her name is Hear-All."

The prince thanked her and went quickly on his way. But no sooner was he among the trees than he heard the Black Dog howling and baying behind him, and once more Merrifyl rode for his life.

But fast though he rode, he could not get away from the Black Dog, and eventually Merrifyl knew that he could not escape.

Just at that moment, when all seemed lost, Merrifyl caught sight of another gipsy caravan. Beside it stood an old gipsy woman tending a fire in a three-legged fire-basket.

"Hide me, hide me," he pleaded, "for the Black Dog is close on my heels."

Exactly as before, the gipsy told Merrifyl to hide in the ash-hole under the fire. Then when the Black Dog appeared, the gipsy drew a long whip from her belt, and a little, white whippet bitch came running up; together whippet and whip drove the terrible animal back into the trees.

In the morning, the gipsy wished Merrifyl good-bye and gave him the whippet, whose name was See-All.

The next night yet another gipsy saved him, and she, too, gave him a little whippet dog, who was called Spring-All. But that wasn't all she gave him.

"Take this ball of wool and this magic wand," she said when Merrifyl was in the saddle and ready to go. "Throw the ball of wool between your horse's ears and follow it wherever it unwinds. Keep the magic wand safe—it will help you when no sword will!"

Merrifyl threw the wool through his horse's ears as the gipsy had told him and galloped after it as it unwound. It led him to the bank of a wide, swift river.

"Now what can I do?" groaned Merrifyl. "The Black Dog is only a few minutes behind me and there is no bridge that I can see."

Just then he remembered the magic wand. So he took it from his belt and struck the water with it. Immediately, a bridge rose from under the water.

Quickly, quickly Merrifyl and his three little whippets dashed across to the other side. Then Merrifyl struck the water with the magic wand and as the Black Dog came bounding down to the river bank, the bridge sank silently out of sight.

Prince Merrifyl rode on until he came to a great, white castle. It was the home of the king of this country and he made Prince Merrifyl very welcome.

What was more, the king had a beautiful young daughter, with hair the colour of corn in the late autumn, and eyes the colour of the sea under a cloudless, sunny sky.

The moment she and Prince Merrifyl saw each other they fell in love and, happily, the king was delighted and agreed they should marry the very next month.

In the meantime, Merrifyl spent his days hunting with the king. All went well until two days before the wedding. That day the hunt went badly.

"There's nothing worth hunting on this side of the river at all," complained the king to his chief huntsman. "If only we could get across to the forest on the other side."

"Ah, but we can!" laughed Merrifyl. "Watch." Merrifyl drew the magic wand from his belt and struck the water with it. Immediately the bridge rose from the depths of the river. The hunting party crossed to the other side and Merrifyl lowered the bridge again.

So far so good, but when, hours later, the party returned, Merrifyl was in such a hurry to see his princess again that he completely forgot to lower the bridge after them.

In fact, he didn't remember it until next morning, and by that time the Black Dog of the Wild Forest had not only crossed the river but had found a wicked old woman who lived in the royal castle and persuaded her to help him to kill the prince.

The old woman agreed to lock Hear-All, See-All and Spring-All in a dark cellar so that Merrifyl would have to go hunting without them.

"Good," growled the Black Dog. "Without them to help him I should be able to handle young Merrifyl. But—just in case things go wrong—this is what you must do."

The second part of his plan was so secret that he whispered it: you must wait and see what it was.

Well, morning came and Prince Merrifyl went out hunting as usual; but without his three dogs. The Black Dog, meanwhile, had already returned across the bridge and lay in wait for the prince. This time Merrifyl was careful to lower the bridge after him; but as he galloped away from the river, something very odd happened. For the old gipsy's magic wand, which was tucked very securely into his belt, somehow managed to slip out and fall to the ground.

All day the Black Dog followed Merrifyl, waiting for his chance to catch him alone. Finally, it came. The prince got lost in the forest: he called the huntsmen, he blew his hunting horn, but nobody seemed to hear.

Nobody, that is, except the Black Dog—who came ravening in to attack the young prince—and, far away in the deep cellar, Hear-All, the little white whippet.

Frantically, she and the other whippets began to bite and scratch at the door. In a moment they wore through. Then they rushed to the river: there was no sign of the prince, and no sign of the bridge, either.

Luckily, See-All spotted the wand lying in the grass; Spring-All leaped across the river and used it to raise the bridge, and all three of them hurried to Merrifyl's rescue.

They arrived just in time—and attacked! Inside a minute, the terrible Black Dog lay dead on the ground, while the prince looked on in surprise.

Later that day the Black Dog's body was burned in the palace courtyard; and the next morning Merrifyl and his princess were married.

But, while everyone was dancing and laughing and eating in the Great Hall, the wicked old woman who had helped the Black Dog was busy raking through his ashes. At last she found what she sought—that is, she found what the Black Dog had told her to look for: a tiny magic bone from his paw.

Carefully she hid it up her sleeve; then she went to join the wedding guests. She made her way through the crowd until she stood right behind Merrifyl and, when he turned to speak to the princess, she popped the Black Dog's bone into his ear.

Instantly Merrifyl fell to the ground.

"He's dead," the old woman screamed in triumph. "The Black Dog has won after all!"

But for all his cleverness, the Black Dog had forgotten one thing: See-All! The Little dog sadly licked her master's dead face . . . then gave an excited bark. She had seen the bone. Quickly she licked it from Merrifyl's ear, and at once the prince opened his eyes and yawned. He was alive!

Well, that's the end of the story—except for one thing, perhaps the strangest part of all. For when, some time after, Prince Merrifyl was taking his young wife back to his own land, his three little whippets suddenly raced ahead of him, turned, and barred the way.

"Stop. We will not let you pass! You must cut off our heads," said Hear-All.

"Cut off your heads?" stammered Merrifyl in amazement. He had never heard a dog speak before. "Never! I owe you my life."

"You must!" said all three dogs together. So Merrifyl did it.

At once the three whippets were changed into three pretty young girls—who were very much alive. Where they came from not even the gipsies can say. All that is known is that Merrifyl, his princess, and the three girls went happily on their way.

Yudishthira goes to heaven

This Indian story is probably the oldest dog story, if not the oldest animal story, in all literature. It comes from the Mahabharata, a great Hindu religious epic composed between 2000 and 3000 BC.

Yudishthira, his brothers Nakula, Sahadev, Arjuna and Bhuma, and their sister Draupadi, had ruled over India for thirty-six years.

They had been good years; years of happiness and prosperity, when the people had gathered in the harvests in peace and safety, when artists had laboured to beautify palaces, temples and lesser buildings, and when the cause of justice had thrived throughout the land. There had been riches, but they had come to seem unimportant—indeed, they were generally despised.

Men lived lives of simple contentment and, if many became priests and holy men, many more still, with just as much honour, did their work, brought up their families, and lived ordinary day-to-day lives.

Then, one day, the brothers and their sister, the queen, met under the cool shade of a banyan tree to discuss the future.

"Clearly there is nothing left for us to do in India," said Yudishthira. "We have worked well; India has no more need of us."

"It only remains for us to make our last journey in this world," said Draupadi.

"Our last journey in this world—and out of it," answered Yudishthira. "A pilgrimage it shall be, a pilgrimage to Heaven."

Now at these words there came a slight sound. Some might describe it as a sniff—a sniff of disapproval. But of course this could not be, for were not the six individuals having this conference among the most perfect men and women who ever lived? So who could disapprove of them?

But sniff it undoubtedly was, followed by a whine—soft and appealing. For someone else was present. Not a king or a queen, not a man or woman at all. Just a little dog—Yudishthira's dog.

History does not record his breed, but he had always been the loyal friend and companion of his master and he hated the thought of being parted from him now.

The little animal knew very well that there could be no place in Heaven for him. Hindus then—as now—had a low opinion of dogs: dogs were unclean, their touch defiled, their presence desecrated. How could such an animal seek entry into Heaven?

All these thoughts went through the minds of dog and master in that moment. But Yudishthira's pilgrimage could not be postponed or neglected for that. His course now lay towards another world, and nothing could stop him.

So, the empire was handed over to new rulers and the five brothers and their royal sister set off on a journey which could only end in their deaths. Up and up they climbed into the mighty Himalaya mountains. Soon, time ceased to have meaning for them as even the clouds were left far below.

One by one the company began to die, fainting and falling away into peaceful oblivion.

At last, only Yudishthira and his faithful dog remained. Together they climbed higher, ever higher, towards the stars, towards the heavens. The man dreamed of paradise; the dog—of who knows what?

At long last their journey came to an end. There was a peal of thunder, then another, and another, and another. The whole mountain range seemed to become one rolling sea of noise, one sweeping symphony of thunder, while below them great grey masses of clouds wheeled through the sky. They had reached the gates of Heaven.

Then before them they saw a great light; all the gold, all the silver, and all the colours from all the precious gems that ever were or ever will be could not equal that light. It flowed over them and round them, it warmed them and cooled them, fed them and made them hungry all at once.

In the centre, where the light was brightest, they saw him standing in his chariot: Indra, King of Heaven, come to take Yudishthira as a living man into Heaven. Yudishthira, who had lived a life without sin: a life which contained no one single act of cruelty or injustice, indifference or greed.

"Come—I have been waiting for you," said Indra. "Stand by me, Yudishthira—perfect one. Heaven and eternal life await you." Then Indra held out his hand and beckoned, inviting Yudishthira to join him.

But Yudishthira stopped and raised his hand.

"Wait, I will not go without my dear brothers and my sister. They fell along the way. Recall them that they may go with us."

"That will not be necessary," answered Indra. "They died indeed, but they have gone before you to Paradise."

"Then I will come," said Yudishthira, and he stepped aside to let his little dog jump into Indra's chariot.

"No, wait!" This time it was Indra's turn to make conditions. "No dog can enter the Kingdom of Heaven. Do I need to tell you the holy scripture? The dog is unclean. Turn him away."

"That I will not do," answered Yudishthira. "Though you be Indra and your chariot awaits, and with it an eternity of happiness and joy, yet I will not go with you if to do so I must turn away this little dog who has spent all his life with me. He has loved me without reserve, whether fortune was with me or not; he has kept faith with me in times of loss and disaster, danger and solitude; he has climbed this mountain with me with no help but his own strength and the unshakable desire never to be parted from me."

The little dog looked up at his master in gratitude, and wagged his tail.

"Shall I turn him from me now, when at last I can repay him?" Yudishthira went on. "Do you ask me at the last to commit an act of indifference, of cruelty and injustice?"

"I ask you to commit no sin," replied Indra. "I ask you only to accept the power of one greater than yourself. Do not gamble over your place in Heaven—no dog can enter here. You must turn him away."

"Then I tell you again that I will not," said Yudishthira, "for all the reasons I have already given, which should be enough, mighty Indra, and for another reason, too. Without my dog this Heaven you offer me would be no Heaven. No, because to be deprived of the companion and friend of so many years would be a bitter loss that even eternal life could not make sweet—indeed, would make all the more bitter. For I would have all time to reflect on his absence and the shortness of his own days compared with my own.

"But there is more still," Yudishthira went on. "What Heaven could there be for me if I were tormented by the memory of how I had turned my friend aside at the last; how I had left him when joy beckoned; how I had sacrificed him for my own happiness? Is this the Heaven you offer? Heaven bought with another's sacrifice, another's loss? Heaven won by bringing pain to a creature who brought always love?

"If this little dog would defile Heaven by his presence, think how much more he would defile Heaven by his absence! Why Heaven would no longer deserve the name, for it would have been tainted for all time by this act of mine, and this request of yours."

Now the thunder roared louder and Yudishthira felt it pressing in on him as if his soul were being crushed into a little space. Indra spoke again:

"Yet I do refuse this dog entry! Even to speak of it is blasphemy. Even a glance from him would defile the sacred places. He shall not pass! Nor can I accept your arguments. Are they not born of pride, O mighty king? At the last aren't you committing one sin: refusing to be ruled by another, refusing to be ruled by me?"

"You know how much pride I have and have not, Indra, blessed one," replied Yudishthira. "And if I sinned in pride I would not now be standing before you with your chariot awaiting me and the doors of Heaven open to receive me. All my life I have known only one emotion: love, and I have sought for that alone, together with peace and justice for all. I cannot give these things up for the sake of Heaven, because for me they *are* Heaven, and there could be no Heaven without them. So I say *No*. I will not go with you. I will return down the mountain and spend the rest of my days in some humble duty, in cold and in hunger if that is my fate, but always in service and charity. My little dog will come with me, and if he dies then I will mourn for him—since he has lived a life of total perfection, as great as any who ever entered Heaven, even though he was refused his reward. Should I die he will mourn me, too, in his way, and do whatever he wants to afterwards while I . . . Well I doubtless shall drift down the river of forgetfulness and become part of the greater elements of the world, neither remembering nor remembered—except for a little time perhaps in this small dog's heart."

For a moment the peals of thunder stopped then, and such a complete silence and stillness fell that it was as if all movement and all time had stopped together.

Then, as Yudishthira stood, to his utter amazement his little dog changed before his eyes. Gone were the white coat, the drooping ears, the quizzical brown eyes, the short tail with the brown tip.

In his place, shining like a dream of white light burning upon spotless snows, stood Dharma, God of Righteousness.

Yudishthira fell upon his knees, but Dharma and Indra raised him up and led him to the chariot, and together they entered it and rode through a great arc of light into Heaven. There Yudishthira was united with his brothers and his sister, and there he lives still in the Hindu Paradise.

Unclean though the dog was held to be, the great God of Righteousness and Justice had not hesitated to take the form of one, and so put Yudishthira to the final test that brought him, a living man, into Heaven.

But perhaps, as he gazes down upon the world and watches the slow ages pass by, perhaps—who knows—even now Yudishthira feels a regret. No sin indeed, but a sadness. For after all, did he not gain Heaven but lose his little dog?

The dog that found his way home

To say that Bobby the collie led an adventurous life would be a very great understatement.

The adventures started when he was still a puppy. In those days Bobby's master, Frank Brazier, lived on a farm near Silverton, in the state of Oregon, USA. One day Bobby undertook to herd one of the farm horses to its stable. Somehow or other the horse, normally a perfectly well-behaved sort of beast, took a violent dislike to the fluffy little fellow who was hustling him along. Its kick landed fair and square on poor Bobby's head, throwing him a good twenty feet away. But when the little puppy finally came to himself, his first thought was for the job he had been doing when the accident happened. Shaky though he was, he got up and saw the horse into the stable.

Adventure number two came soon after. Bobby quickly recovered from the kick and was fast regaining his strength when he quarrelled with another important part of the farmyard scene: the tractor.

This encounter was even more serious than the one with the horse: the tractor ran over his legs and injured him badly. Again, he was not discouraged, and in a month he was fit again.

Fit, that is, for his next adventure. For Frank Brazier sold his farm and became a restaurant owner in town.

"A restaurant is no place for a dog like Bobby," thought Frank, and sold both his dog and his farm to the same buyer.

Frank didn't ask Bobby what he thought about all this, but the moment Bobby realized he had been left behind he made his opinion quite plain. At the first opportunity, the collie ran away. Straight to his old master, Frank.

Well, Frank took him back to his new master, but Bobby ran away a second time, then a third. In fact, it became such a habit that in the end Frank admitted defeat and bought the dog back again.

The scene was now set for the greatest of all Bobby's adventures, an adventure that would make him one of the most famous dogs in the world.

It began quietly enough, in August 1923, when he was two years old. He was full-

grown by this time of course, powerful and tough, with all the speed and intelligence of the collie plus a dash of something—including a bob tail—from a little Old English sheepdog blood he had also inherited. That summer Frank Brazier went touring in his car. He took his wife, and he took Bobby.

Like all dogs, Bobby adored riding in a car, sitting for hours looking out of the window with his chin resting on the window ledge.

It was a long, long journey: 2,000 miles eastwards to the state of Indiana. There Frank Brazier stopped his car in the little town of Walcott for oil and petrol. He had made scores of similar stops on the trip, but this was one he would remember all his life.

Full of excitement, Bobby jumped out of the car and raced off to explore. If there was one thing he liked better than a good long car ride, it was arriving in new places and looking around them. He had not roamed very far when he met another dog. Then he met a whole crowd of dogs, a whole scavenging pack of stray dogs in fact. And while Bobby may have been delighted to see a new town these dogs were not at all pleased to see a new dog, especially Bobby.

They attacked him! He fought back of course, for he loved a battle, and many of his attackers regretted taking him on. But what could one dog—even one as brave and effective at fighting as Bobby—do against so many?

Slowly they drove him back, attacking in greater and greater numbers until he had no other choice but to run for it, with the whole band of dogs howling at his heels. From time to time he turned and counter-attacked—so fiercely that in the end the other dogs gave up the chase. Bobby's fighting retreat finally amounted to a great victory. He had won. But . . .

He was lost!

Breathing heavily he looked around him. It was late and the sun was sinking. All was quiet, and utterly, utterly unrecognizable. Bobby didn't know where he was, or how he got there. One thing he did know though: he was miles from where he had started, miles from his master who must certainly be wondering what had happened to him.

Bobby was right! Far away, at the garage, Frank Brazier was pacing up and down. Where was that dog? He and his wife went searching for him all over the little town and as far as the furthest suburbs.

"Have you seen a black-and-white collie with a bob tail?" they asked wherever they went. But nobody remembered any dog like that! Still they searched, but still they found no trace.

"It's no good. We don't know where he is or what he's doing," Mrs. Brazier said. "We have to go on."

"Yes, I suppose so," Frank replied sadly, "but I hate going without Bobby. There must be something else we can do."

"Why not put an advertisement in the local newspaper then," said Mrs. Brazier, "and offer a reward to anyone who finds Bobby or helps to find him."

"Good idea; and I'll leave some money at the railway station too, so that he can be sent home if ever he does turn up."

The Braziers took one last look round the town, then went on their way. They drove southwards: from Indiana and the shores of the Great Lakes, to Mexico. Then they turned west and north, along the Pacific coast, and so to Oregon and home.

It was a good trip, a marvellous trip, but a sad trip also; and it would have been even sadder had the Braziers known what was happening to Bobby.

For the young collie was lost—lost in the middle of a great continent, with 2,000 of the toughest miles in the United States between himself and home. Even the first step back was a difficult one: finding the garage where he had left his master.

Having done that (there was no sign of the Braziers now, of course), Bobby set out on his great journey. At first he went south: that is, *away* from home. Perhaps he was following the Braziers' car. Perhaps at that time he was as lost as any human being would have been in the same circumstances.

In fact, for the next three months, Bobby literally wandered in circles! West was the direction he needed to go, and though he travelled 1,000 miles in this period he went only 400 miles in a westerly direction.

It was when he arrived in Kansas City that everything changed for Bobby.

There he suddenly found himself caught up in a mad scramble of dogs and people, all centred on the wire-caged waggon of the local dog-catcher, who was busy rounding up strays.

Bobby a stray? Probably no dog in history ever tried so hard *not* to be a stray. The chase was desperate, but in the end he was caught and flung headlong into the hated waggon, full of whining, barking, fighting and frightened dogs.

But even as a puppy, Bobby had known what had to be done, and had done it, and he had not changed. He had been almost knocked out but what did that matter? If the horse on the farm hadn't been able to knock the determination out of him, no town dog-catcher could!

So, when the door of the waggon was opened Bobby got on with it: with a supreme effort he hurled himself at the human barrier that stood between him and freedom, and somehow burst through. Free!

Now he was off like the wind. From somewhere there came to him all the instinctive, incredible ability of dogs to find their way home. In six days, running almost non-stop he reached the city of Denver, Colorado, 550 miles from where he had been caught.

This was tough country: before him the Rocky mountains reached high, and beyond them stretched the deserts of Utah. Still he battled on, crossing the mountains in the depths of winter in spite of the blizzards and the icy rivers that swirled across his path.

Several times he nearly died of starvation or exposure, but the game little collie never gave up. Whenever he found his strength absolutely failing he managed to find his way to a farm or lumber camp, or to a house in some isolated country town. He always found someone prepared to give him a place by the fire and a good meal. But never once did he stop anywhere longer than the time required to gather his strength.

Sometimes in his weakness he wandered off the line of his route—perhaps when he had to make a detour to avoid a swamp, or was forced to search for water in a desert; or when he was chased by another dog-catcher.

At last, on 15th February 1924, six months to the day since he had jumped out of his master's car, Bobby—thin, exhausted, dust-covered, his feet cut and bleeding—staggered to Frank Brazier's door.

He was nearly dead from hunger, thirst and cold. He could not stand without help, and it was a whole week before his feet had healed enough—and he had strength enough—to walk.

He had done it. He had come home. Through the heat of summer and the bitter cold of a bad winter, he had come 2,000 miles in six months.

But, though his tour was over, Bobby's legend was only just beginning. Newspapers began writing about him, thousands of people came to see him, or wrote letters or telephoned. Medals and awards and gifts poured in from all over the world.

The young collie was famous, and even if there were times when he and Frank Brazier felt that the problems of fame were worse than those of crossing the Rocky mountains in winter, it did have one wholly pleasurable side to it: all over the United States people remembered seeing Bobby, remembered helping him with food and shelter. Now those people knew just how important a part they had played in his greatest adventure. Bobby had not only created a legend, he had also made many, many friends.

Vigi the Viking

There are many stories and legends about Olaf Tryggvason the dashing and often cruel Viking hero. He was the first man successfully to introduce Christianity to Norway and in 994 he became the first man to unite the country—with himself as king. Just six years later he was overthrown in battle. There is a legend that Olaf was not actually killed but swam ashore safely. However, he had lost his kingdom and, being too overcome with grief to attempt to win it back, he retired to Greece where he lived as a hermit. None of the stories explain why Vigi, his dog, was not with his master in his fight: one possible reason is suggested here.

All round the hall the Vikings were singing, singing of Olaf Tryggvason, King of Norway, and his dog Vigi. For these were Olaf's men, 600 in all: friends and fellow Vikings, soldiers and sailors, the crew and complement of Olaf's great dragon-ship, the *Long Serpent*.

In the centre of the hall a fire blazed, the smoke rising to a single square louvre in the oak-beamed roof above. Below, two deer were roasting on spits over the fire.

All around were set trestle tables forming three sides of a hollow square; the fourth side was in the form of a raised dais on which a heavier, richly ornamented table was set. This was Olaf's table.

The Vikings finished their song and began talking and joking among themselves.

"I knew Olaf in Russia—that's longer than anyone else here!" shouted Haakon, one of the few dark-haired Vikings.

"Hey, I was there too," shouted back Gunnar, whose hair was as yellow as corn. "What's more, I went with him to Greece while you were lying wounded in Bergen on your father's farm."

"But neither of you was with him on the Irish raid," said Harald, "when he bought Vigi, whom even now we sing of."

At that they all fell to drinking the health of Olaf and Vigi, and telling the story of how they came to meet. Most of the time, though, they listened to Kolbjörn. He was the best story-teller of them all, and, like Harald, he had been on the famous raid to Ireland where it had all begun.

"It was six years ago, in 994," Kolbjörn said. "We raided England that year, sailing right up the Thames as far as London. The English paid us to go away, as usual, only this time Olaf promised never to go raiding there again. Then we set off for home. Olaf told us before we started that he was going to make himself King of Norway, but he wasn't in so much of a hurry to get back that he would pass up a good chance of another raid on the way.

"So we decided to pay a call on the Irish."

"What is it the English say of us?" interrupted Sigurd Knutsen. "'From the fury of the Norsemen, good Lord deliver us.' Do the Irish say that too?"

"Probably. But there wasn't too much fury that time, and the Irish did their own delivering," replied Kolbjörn. "The Irish had really learned to fight: they kept bringing up more and more fresh men and retreating slowly until they had a forest at their back, a river on one flank, and their village on the other.

"But they hadn't been able to take their cattle with them in their retreat. So we rounded them all up and set off back to the boats before anything serious happened. This time it was the Irish who left *us* alone! Well, we were driving those great shaggy Irish beasts along when suddenly up popped an Irishman—a big man he was, with red hair. How he got through our skirmish line I'll never know, but there he was. Before anyone could stop him he marched straight up to Olaf himself. Well, you know Olaf. The man was lucky not to be cut down before he opened his mouth. But he said his piece—short and to the point.

"'See here, sir,' he said, 'you have taken my twenty cows, and without them I'll die. Let me have my twenty back!'

"At first Olaf treated it as some sort of joke: 'Come man, you won't starve,' he said.

"But the Irishman was adamant: 'No sir, I'll die, and so will my family. Come, let me have my cattle back. What are twenty more or less to you?'

"'Indeed, we wouldn't miss them,' agreed Olaf. 'Take your twenty back—but only *your* twenty mind—you must identify each beast as your own.'

"'They have my own special ear-nick,' said the Irishman.

"'Good,' answered Olaf, 'but how are you going to find so few among so many?'

"'That's easy. My dog here will soon pick them out,' the man replied. With that he gave a whistle and through the crowd of men and animals came running a shaggy-coated dog. 'Find, find, Vigi!' cried the Irishman, and off Vigi went.

"That was the first time any of us ever saw Vigi. How he managed it I still can't understand to this day, but in a minute or two he'd counted out exactly twenty cattle from the hundreds we'd rounded up, all with the Irishman's special ear-nick.

"Then Olaf took off a great gold bracelet he wore on his arm—worth the whole herd put together I should think—and bought Vigi with it."

So Vigi the Irish cattle-dog became Vigi the Viking, beloved of all the crewmen of the *Long Serpent*, with whom he shared all the danger and discomfort of battles and voyages alike.

From the first, Vigi was Olaf's inseparable companion. On board ship they lived and ate and slept side by side, and in battle, Vigi would stay close to his master while he directed the fighting or struggled hand-to-hand with the enemy.

In all the time Vigi and Olaf were together, no battle was more fierce, no service of Vigi's was more valuable, than when Olaf fought with Thore Hjart and Raud the Strong. These two great chieftains were bitterly opposed to Olaf uniting Norway under his crown, and they led their own powerful fleets against him. There was a great battle which Olaf clearly won. Seeing themselves defeated, Raud fled in one direction while Thore—with Olaf in hot pursuit—flew in another.

For hours they raced across the choppy northern seas, but gradually Olaf edged closer and closer until Thore was forced to steer for land. He reached the shore first, and hurriedly beached his boat.

Olaf leaped on to the beach and raced after him. But Thore had a good start, and would have escaped if it hadn't been for Vigi, who hurled himself on the man just as it looked as if he was going to get away. Thore turned and stabbed Vigi to the ground with his spear, but at that moment Olaf came to his dog's rescue and killed Thore with a single blow.

To Olaf, however, it seemed a poor

triumph. His enemy lay dead, but so too did Vigi, his dearest friend. When the rest of his men came up, the king ordered them to carry Vigi back to the ship.

"On a shield—carry him on a shield, like the warrior he was," said Olaf.

Sadly the procession moved off, the men with their heads bowed, carrying the heavy wooden shield on which lay the motionless Vigi. Sadly, too, stood the ship's crew as the shield was set down on the deck.

"Alas, this is our greatest loss in all the fighting," someone said. "We must bury him like a hero."

The Vikings turned sadly away. Then they heard something! A faint bark!

As one man they whirled around. There was Vigi, sitting up and looking rather surprised. He had enjoyed the shield ride very much. Why had it stopped, he wanted to know. He barked again: "A ride! A ride!"

Laughing, the Vikings lifted the shield again and carried it in triumph up and down the deck, with Vigi barking strongly now, and seeming to pay no attention at all to the ugly-looking wound in his shoulder where Thore's spear had caught him.

"Well, that's how it happened," went on Kolbjörn, "and ever since, you only have to show a shield to Vigi for him to want to have a ride on it. Afterwards we followed Raud—and caught him too. But it was a long chase in the worst weather that I ever saw. We were lucky to get back alive."

At that very moment a hush fell upon the hall. The musicians stopped their playing, men paused with food half way to their mouths or in the very act of chewing and swallowing. They had heard a well-known bark.

Then the great oak door swung open, and a tall young man strode in. Behind him there stalked a large shaggy dog . . .

"OLAF! OLAF! OLAF!" chanted the Vikings, as Olaf Tryggvason, King of Norway, strode forward and stood in front of the table on the dais. He raised his hands for silence, and Vigi gave a commanding bark.

"Countrymen—Norseman—fellow Vikings," said Olaf. "Before I join the feast I have news for you. In two days' time we sail for the land of the Wends, either to talk or to fight—I don't know which—but, either way, to force them to pay my wife the money she is owed from her lands in their kingdom."

The Vikings cheered and clapped at this. They all felt they had been idle too long.

Olaf sat down and removed his helmet of gilded iron. His hair was yellow, his eyes blue; he wore a long coat of chain mail with a scarlet silk tunic over it. Vigi sat with his head resting on his master's knees.

"Vigi, my brother," Olaf said looking down, "alas I must leave you behind on this trip. Every man I can trust in Norway is coming—someone must be left behind whom I can rely on not to betray me. Stay here and guard my house."

Vigi's head drooped and he crawled beneath the table. All through that evening, no matter how often or how hard he tried, Olaf could not rouse his dog or cheer him up.

If only Vigi could have spoken! He could have told Olaf of the strange sense of foreboding he had of deadly danger. He would have said, "Don't go. Something terrible will happen if you do. Stay here!"

But Vigi could not speak, and in time Olaf made his trip to Wendland. It was successful, but as he sailed home the *Long Serpent* was ambushed by a mighty fleet of Danes, Swedes and rebel Norsemen. It was a long fierce battle and had Olaf been fighting the Danes and Swedes alone perhaps his furious courage would have carried the day. But in the end the king and all his brave company were overcome.

The reign of Olaf of Norway was over, and Vigi followed him to the grave soon after.

But neither has been forgotten. For the Norwegians still say that one day if their country is invaded and they are in peril, Olaf and Vigi will return and save them.

Rip, the first rescue dog

It was over, and once again the howl of the sirens told the people of the city that it was safe to come out of their cellars and shelters and return to bed. For many people, however, the real night's work was only just beginning.

This was war; the year 1940, the place London; and the raid that had just taken place had been a particularly heavy one. Bomber squadrons had come sweeping in from the south and east, from the direction of France and Belgium and Holland, and they had struck hard at the factories, the railways, and the docks.

Defending fighter aircraft had engaged them, and dozens of desperate battles had been fought thousands of feet above the ground. But below, among the narrow streets and small houses of the men who worked at the dockyards or on the railways, an equally desperate battle had taken place, and unlike the battle in the sky, it didn't end when the bombers turned for home.

For on the ground the fires still raged, while teams of men struggled to rescue survivors from beneath the ruins of their homes.

In the dock areas things were worst of all. Hardly a street seemed to have escaped damage of some sort, and often whole rows of houses had been devastated, and now lay in ruins or blazed furiously.

Everywhere there was the smell of burning, and although the echoes of the exploding bombs and the rattle of gunfire had now died away, the air was loud with the sound of bells and sirens: fire engines, ambulances, rescue squads, army bomb-disposal teams.

In Poplar in East London, where many of the docks were, the smoke—from burning houses and dock buildings—was at its thickest. The roads and pavements were filled with the twisting shapes of hundreds of hosepipes, and with fallen bricks, roof slates and glass.

There was an enormous amount of work to do, and the men who had to do it were strained to breaking point.

It was then that Rip first appeared. He just turned up at the command headquarters of the Air Raid Precautions force in Southill Street. No one knew where he came from or what had happened to his real owners. Perhaps they lay buried under the wreckage of their home? Perhaps they were safe but homeless? Perhaps Rip had simply lost them?

"Who's this?" grunted one of the men there, noticing him. "What's happened to you, mate?" he asked, and patted the bewildered and dusty dog who stood looking up at him in the doorway.

The dog slowly wagged his tail, then sat down. Wherever he had come from, he looked as if he were making himself at home.

"I'll look after him for a bit if you like," another man said. "I'll give him something to eat, then we'll see how he feels—I expect he'll go off after. But let's have a look at that collar anyway. He might have a name."

Indeed the dog did have a name: Rip.

"Well Rip," said the man, taking off his steel helmet and sitting himself on an upturned box, "we haven't got much, but you're welcome. Have some of this meat pie for a start."

How long it had been since he first started wandering the streets nobody knew, but he didn't seem to have eaten for a long time. In fact, Rip was starving, and he gulped down his share of the pie in a second. He gulped down several thick slices of bread, too, before he began to look satisfied.

When he had finished, the man, whose name was Edward King, gave him a good drink of water, patted him on the shoulder, and stood aside to let him leave.

But to his surprise, Rip showed no sign of wanting to go. Instead he stretched himself out comfortably and had a good rest before doing a quick inspection of the small command post. There wasn't much to see, but evidently he liked what there was.

From that moment, Rip adopted Southill Road ARP, and he adopted Edward King too. Even so, it was some time before the men at the post knew just what a valuable recruit Rip was.

It was a little later, after another particularly bad raid, and the ARP men were desperately hacking at the collapsed ruins of a building. They dug, they listened, they probed with long rods; then they dug and listened again. They were searching for survivors lying injured under the wreckage—and they were also searching for the dead.

Suddenly Edward King glanced up. Rip was acting rather strangely. He was sniffing keenly at a mass of tangled girders and fallen brick, and pawing at it as if trying to tear it apart himself.

Mr. King's eyes met Rip's, and the dog barked eagerly, expectantly.

"Quick lads," cried Edward King, "get into that spot there—winch that girder off—I think Rip's found someone!"

Sure enough, Rip had; and again and again that night he found someone. Rip seemed to be able to locate people, dead or alive, even if they were completely buried under debris. Never once did he make a mistake.

So it went on—raid after raid, rescue after rescue.

"Every rescue team should have a dog like Rip," someone said one day as the men toiled at their job. For not only did the wiry little mongrel save much time and effort by directing the diggers to the right places, but he saved lives too: many people would have remained buried, or would have been buried far longer, without him.

Now the remarkable thing in all this was that Rip was entirely untrained in rescue work or tracking. Everything he ever did he did because of his own instinct.

Nor did Rip's work start and finish with rescues. During all the raid alerts he stayed on duty with the ARP men, patrolling the streets, watching for the fall of incendiary bombs and giving warning of fires, marking unexploded bombs, and seeing that everyone kept under cover.

At night he always went with his master as he toured the street shelters—the cellars and the brick and concrete bunkers built to protect people from the bombs.

This could be nerve-wracking work; for even if the night was peaceful blackout laws were very strict. No-one was allowed to use a light outside and at times the streets were absolutely dark. Wardens like Edward were permitted to use a blue-coloured torch from time to time, but even so most of them stumbled around in the dark from one shelter to another. Edward and Rip usually did far better however, for Rip had a wonderful knack for threading his way between hidden obstacles. He avoided new debris from the last raid as easily as longer-established and better-known dangers.

If a raid were in progress the patrols were more alarming still, of course, for bombs would suddenly swish out of the sky. Rip learned to distinguish the more dangerous high-explosive bombs' sound from that of the smaller incendiaries. There would also be a constant rain of shrapnel, caused by the air-bursting of shells from the anti-aircraft guns, but somehow Rip never seemed to be troubled by this.

Gradually, more and more rescue dogs began to appear in the streets of London and the other great cities. Together they saved the lives of hundreds of people, and hundreds of animals too. But to Rip goes the honour of being absolutely the first.

He worked solidly for five years at his self-appointed task, from that day in 1940 until the end of the war. Of course, there were a couple of quiet years in the middle of this period, when the raids stopped almost completely, but the patrols had to be mounted just the same and all the blackout regulations were strictly enforced. Then at the end there was the terror of the flying bombs and rockets to face.

Nothing could deter Rip, however, and every night he helped to reassure people in the crowded shelters and packed cellars, usually getting a titbit of some sort as a reward.

Sadly, Rip did not live for very long after the war. He was not a young dog even at the very beginning of his great career, and though no one ever discovered his true age, he must have been quite old when he died in the autumn of 1946.

Happily, however, Rip had already had his reward. At the end of the war in 1945 the organization called the People's Dispensary for Sick Animals (PDSA) awarded him their Dickin Medal, for bravery, the highest award that any animal can win in Britain.

ogne
LA BONHEUR DU

The dog and his master's dinner

La Fontaine, from whose *Fables* this story is adapted, spent much of his life in Paris. Because of this, and because there may have been a real-life model for Trusty, the story is set against a background of the Ile de la Cité and the Left Bank in Paris. The time is the mid-seventeenth century.

Trusty the setter looked up at his master and smiled. At least, he came as near smiling as a dog can, and his master understood.

"Here's the money, old boy," said his master, Paul the gunsmith. "Now take it to the big café with the blue shutters and collect my lunch. Off you go now—when you come back you shall have a taste!"

With that, Paul patted Trusty's head, dropped a large silver coin into a canvas bag, and hung it around the setter's neck.

Trusty didn't really need to be told what to do, for this was a regular routine between him and his master. Every day at noon, Paul would carefully put down the gun he was working on, take some money from his pocket, and send Trusty off to the café with the blue shutters to buy his lunch.

Naturally, the people at the café knew what Trusty had come for, so he didn't have to do any explaining. One of the waiters would open the bag, take out the money, and replace it with a clip-topped earthenware container with that day's special dish in it. Then Trusty would hurry home so that the food was still piping hot when he arrived.

On Sundays, when Paul's workshop was closed, he and Trusty would go together to the café, return all the containers from the week, and stay for a special Sunday lunch: four good courses for Paul, a big dish of meat and vegetables for Trusty.

Paul's workshop was in a small street near the river; there were two rooms upstairs where Paul and Trusty lived, and two rooms downstairs where Paul worked. His storeroom was in the cellar. Paul's workshop was simply crammed from floor to ceiling with guns of every shape and kind: long-barrelled muskets for hunting, short carbines to be carried by horsemen, and a dozen sizes of pistols. Most of the guns had highly polished wooden stocks; and all were carved, engraved, and decorated with tracery and moulding in brass and silver and gold.

Trusty was very proud of his master, who was famous among the craftsmen of the city. Many times as he was hurrying home with Paul's lunch, other dogs would trot alongside him and ask about Paul, or Paul's lunch, or Paul's business.

"Gerruff! How are you, Trusty my boy?" was how Papa the old bulldog always began conversations. "How's it goin', eh? That young master of yours still keepin' you at it? Clever chap though, and I suppose he feeds you well, eh? What?"

But Trusty made no reply and kept running along. He liked Paul to have his food good and hot. He had no time for idle chatter at a time like this!

Then there was Maud the poodle. "Oh, my dear Trusty, what a surprise! How very nice to meet you," she would say, despite the fact that she saw Trusty at the same time in the same place nearly every day. "Hmm, that smells good. Now don't tell me what it is—let me guess. Chicken stew with dumplings perhaps? Or roast beef with vegetables? Or perhaps a sole with cream and grapes? Whatever it is, Paul is going to like it, I feel sure."

Trusty only answered her with a snort of disdain. He had a very low opinion of any animal who couldn't tell the difference in smells between chicken stew, roast beef, or sole with cream and grapes; and in any case he couldn't waste time chatting.

Then there was Boris the dalmatian. Boris belonged to a banker, and he seemed to make it his business to pry into everyone else's.

"Hello, Trusty. How's the gun-making business these days? You should be doing very nicely just now. Good, good. But remember if Paul ever needs a small loan to tide him over—what shall I say?—a difficult period, why not send him along to us? I'm sure my master would oblige!"

But Trusty just grunted and never said a word.

That's how the trip back from the café usually was. But today, although Trusty didn't know it yet, things were going to be different.

Not that anything happened at first. Trusty raced off to the café as usual. There the waiter took the money from the bag around Trusty's neck and replaced it with a big pot of delicious beef stew.

Not for the first time, Trusty wished he could eat all the lunch himself. But, trusty as ever, he overcame his longings and hurried out of the café.

He had just crossed back over the bridge into the quarter of the town where the workshop was, when the trouble started.

Orlov! A great dane. The greatest great dane in all the city, and just about the worst-tempered anywhere!

"Oh dear, here's someone I could do without meeting," thought Trusty to himself. "I hope he doesn't notice me."

But notice Trusty he did. Which wasn't really surprising since he was standing where he was for no other purpose than to wait for Trusty. The day before, Papa and Maud and Boris had gone to see him and made a certain suggestion.

"Look, Orlov, my old friend . . ." Boris had begun.

"Friend nothing! I haven't got any friends!" growled Orlov.

"Er, just a figure of speech," Boris went on. "Listen, how would you like to get your teeth into Paul the gunsmith's lunch? He has it brought every day from the café with the blue shutters?"

"Ah, I would like it very much," Orlov said.

So the plot began; and that was why on that fateful day, as Trusty came hurrying along with his master's beef stew tucked under his chin, Orlov was waiting for him. Meanwhile, lurking in the background, Papa, Maud and Boris were waiting for Orlov.

They had mostly come to watch Trusty's humiliation, but all three of them had a secret hope that perhaps—somehow—they might be able to pick up a little of the gunsmith's lunch for themselves. But none of them said this openly.

Orlov lumbered forward to bar Trusty's way, his lip curled in a threatening sneer.

"What's that you've got there?" he asked.

"Nothing much . . ." muttered Trusty,

trying to slip past Orlov without looking at him. He was skilled in the ways of the town and intended to avoid trouble if he could.

"That's beef stew you've got there," snarled the great dane. "From the café—and I'm having it, see?"

Trusty was trapped. He could either fight, or drop the lunch and run.

He decided to fight. Quickly ducking his head out of the sling of the bag, he faced the bigger dog.

"Stay away from this lunch!" he barked. Then, deciding that against so big an opponent the best defence was attack, he charged the great bullying Orlov.

"Hey, get off me—OUCH!" howled Orlov. Slow-witted and ponderous as he was, fast in-fighting wasn't really Orlov's style.

"If that—UGH!—Boris had told me you could fight like this (*pant, puff*), I'd never have been here—OO!"

"Boris! So he's behind this!" growled Trusty. "Well I hope you're watching, Boris, because when I've finished with this big bully I'm going to come looking for you!"

Boris yelped. He hadn't had any idea Trusty could fight like this either. He looked at Papa and Maud, but both of them edged away: Boris wasn't going to get any help from *them*. But at that moment things took another turn, unexpected by any of the dogs so far involved.

For, attracted by the barking and howling of Orlov and Trusty, a large crowd had gathered—a crowd of men, women and boys, certainly, but above all a crowd of dogs. Dogs that took one look at the battle and dived in.

Not, to be sure, to take part in the fight itself. They dived in to get the food!

"Hey, get away, leave that alone!" shouted Trusty. "Scram! Move off!"

But still they came. More and more. It seemed as if every stray mongrel in the city was rushing to get a bite at a free meal.

Under cover of all the confusion, Orlov slunk away—and you don't see great danes doing that very often. He had had more than enough.

But Trusty—Trusty was surrounded. Desperately he raced round in a circle, a circle with Paul's dinner at its centre. Whenever he approached, the crowd of dogs gave way, but the moment his back was turned they pressed forward again.

It was no good. Trusty was losing.

Trusty had lost! With a leap he shot back to the bag of food.

"You win," he cried. "You can have it. But, since Paul is going to lose his dinner anyway, you can all wait till I have a bit too!"

With that, Trusty stooped and undid first the precious bag, then the clips on the container inside; he took one delicious mouthful of the marvellous stew then, snatching up the bag, rushed away to the edge of the crowd.

There was one enormous, long drawn-out howl, and such a scene of pushing, shoving, jumping and scrambling as had never been seen before.

When it was all over, Trusty collected the broken pieces of the container, dropped them into the bag, and sadly trotted home to his master with the remains.

"Hello, Trusty, you've been a long time," said Paul. "Have you had trouble?"

Trusty put down the bag and slunk into the corner, his head drooping and his tail between his legs.

"You've been fighting, I see—and, ah! you have lost my lunch."

Trusty whined and looked up dolefully.

"You tried to protect my lunch didn't you? Well, never mind. I know you did your best. Come, I'll shut the shop and we will *both* have lunch—together."

So off they went, Paul whistling, and Trusty the setter leaping at his heels.

"Ah, well," thought Trusty to himself, "things didn't turn out too badly after all. Perhaps it's just as well I can't explain exactly what happened."

The Isle of Dogs

In the great city of London, by the river Thames, is a district called the Isle of Dogs. This is how it got its odd name.

"Hello, it's that little dog again."

Farmer Jonathon Pimlico (or so we shall call him for, like the names of all the characters in this story, his real name has long been forgotten) was leaning over the low stone wall around the orchard of his farm, munching an apple and enjoying the autumn sunshine and the view. From where he stood he could see across a great glittering stretch of the river Thames and the fields beyond. Away upstream lay the great city of London. Downstream were Chatham and Gravesend where the king's big ships lay. On all sides the land was rich: patched with the green and gold of the fields, the white of the farmhouses and the pale brown of their thatched roofs.

Today all this area is part of London, and is densely covered with houses and flats, roads, docks, railways. But in Jonathon Pimlico's time, 300 years ago, London was a very small place indeed, and nearly all the area which is now built up was then open country.

Farmer Jonathon's house looked out towards a small island in the river, and the little dog, a black-and-white mongrel, was swimming as fast as he could towards the mainland. Now there was nothing very remarkable in that perhaps; but this little dog made a habit of it!

"Every day this month," Jonathon exclaimed. "Across in the afternoon, back again in the early evening. But where does he go to in between? And why does he go back to that island at all? That's what I can't understand.

"There's more to this than meets the eye," he thought. "Nobody lives on the island, except a duck or two. So whatever does that little dog find to do there?"

As Jonathon watched, the little dog came splashing ashore and set off rapidly along a narrow bridle path leading inland.

Farmer Jonathon went back to picking apples, but he kept his eyes open for the dog's return and, sure enough, two hours or so later, back came the little dog—back to the same spot on the bank—and off he swam to his lonely, muddy island.

Next day, Jonathon was more curious than ever about the little mongrel, so when the familiar black-and-white shape came swimming across from the island, Jonathon decided to follow him.

Now, as you probably know, when dogs walk they go either very fast, or very slowly. This one went fast, never stopping for a moment, or glancing to right or left. Jonathon had great trouble keeping him in sight, and he was almost exhausted, when, after they had gone some miles, the dog arrived at a small farmhouse surrounded by a circle of trees. He went straight up to the front door and barked loudly, several times. Almost at once the door was opened.

Out came a cheerful-looking, red-faced man. He was laughing and carried a large wooden dish piled high with food.

"Aha, my little friend, here you are again," cried the man, smiling broadly.

He set the dish down before the dog and watched while he ate it all. Then, when he had finished, the dog licked his paws, wagged his tail just twice, and ran off back towards the river.

Jonathon made no attempt to follow after him: even if he had wanted to he wouldn't have had the strength. Instead he came out from behind the tree where he had been hiding.

"Good day to you, friend," he said to the red-faced farmer. "Jonathon Pimlico at your service."

"Ah, good day! Ham's the name. I saw you skulking around behind the tree. I was wondering when you'd come out. That your dog was it?"

"No, no," answered Jonathon. "I thought he might be yours. I followed him here from the river."

"The river?"

"Yes, he swims ashore from the island every day. I've been watching him for a month. I can see the river from where I live, you see. I've been puzzled to know where he went to."

"Well, *I've* been wondering just where he came *from*," laughed Farmer Ham. "But you can see why he comes here—for a good meal. He seems to be half-starved, poor thing!"

"Well, there's nothing for a dog to eat on the island," Jonathon said. "Nobody lives there at all, not a soul. Look, I've had an idea: tomorrow when he comes, why don't we both follow him? I'll have a boat ready for us, then we'll take a look at that island and see what that little fellow does on it."

Next day, when the dog plunged into the Thames to swim back to the island, Jonathon and Ham climbed into a dinghy and rowed quietly after him, keeping him just within sight. Now the island was really no more than a mudbank: the only things growing on it were great belts of tall reeds, and by the time Jonathon and Ham had reached the island the dog had vanished into them. However, it was a simple matter to follow his tracks in the soft, marshy ground, and after a few minutes they found him.

He was lying stretched out on a low mound of freshly dug earth.

"Hello there," said Jonathon, "what are you doing all on your own, little fellow? Come, move aside."

The dog gave the two men a forlorn look, then slowly stood up . . . and stayed where he was.

Then Ham tried: "Come boy, come. I'm your friend, remember? I wouldn't hurt you. Just move over a bit, eh?"

But still the little animal remained where he was.

Ham and Jonathon both pleaded with him, and at last, after what seemed like hours of patting and stroking and wheedling, the little dog raised his black-and-white head and finally walked a few yards away.

The situation was only too clear. Someone had dug a trench, buried something, and refilled the trench again.

"I don't like the look of this at all," Jonathon said grimly. "It looks like . . ."

"Aye, I know what it looks like," said Ham quietly.

Half an hour's digging confirmed their fears—a man had been robbed and murdered and secretly buried on the island. Someone who must surely have been the little dog's master—for why else would he guard the grave so faithfully, and for so long?

Who the dead man was, was never discovered—though the local magistrate (there were no police in those days) made all the enquiries he could. But they brought his body back to the mainland, and had him properly buried in a churchyard near Jonathon's farm and within sight of the island.

The little mongrel left the island then, and Jonathon and Ham shared the job of looking after him. But he didn't really seem able to settle down. He divided his time between staying with Jonathon and Ham, staring across the river at the island, and standing by his master's grave. Fortunately neither man minded this rather strange behaviour and they all became fast friends.

A year later, all three journeyed together up the river to London. Jonathon and Ham wanted to buy and sell at a great Fair which was being held in the city at that time. All went well until they arrived at a landing stage close to the Tower of London. Then something very strange happened.

Without any warning the little dog, always so quiet and gentle, gave a furious bark, and flung himself at one of the men standing on the jetty.

"Get that dog away from me," cried the man. "He's dangerous, he's mad! Get him off me!"

"He's never behaved like this before," cried Jonathon, trying to drag the enraged mongrel away. But all his efforts, and those of Ham, were in vain. A crowd began to gather as, time after time, the little dog broke free from his masters and tore at the man. Suddenly Jonathon understood.

"Seize this man!" he shouted. "Take him before a magistrate! Question him! This dog knows him as the murderer of his master!"

At once the man was seized, and he was taken off and questioned. Sure enough, he finally confessed to having robbed and killed a stranger a year before, and to burying him secretly on the little island. It seemed that he had tried to kill the man's dog too but, unluckily for the murderer, the animal had escaped.

Of course, all this happened long, long ago. The island in the Thames is no longer quite an island, for it is now linked to the shore by a narrow strip of land; and—as you have already heard—no one any longer knows the name of the dog, the friends, or the murderer. The name of the murdered man was never discovered.

But the story of the little dog still lives on, and for hundreds of years the island where he faithfully guarded his master's body has been known as the Isle of Dogs.

Jock and the lost prospector

It was midday, and the sun-scorched hills of the Randall Ranges in Western Australia seemed to throb with the heat of the sun. There were no roads through that wilderness, and hardly a landmark that anyone who wasn't at home in the Outback of Australia would notice.

Certainly Sidney had failed to see any. But then Sidney could hardly be expected to. He was a city dweller, a young man accustomed to the noise and bustle of the fast-growing towns of the coast. Back home Sidney was thought to be rather a clever young man, enterprising and daring.

He had shown both those qualities when he had left home to join in the great rush for gold in Western Australia. For Sidney was just one of thousands of people from all over

the world, who were drawn to the harsh Australian Outback in the 1880s by the hope of finding gold and making their fortune.

So far, however, Sidney had *not* found a fortune, and now it seemed as if his enterprise and daring had led him to disaster.

He was lying in a small fold in the rock, beside a water hole. Where he was, how he had got there and how he was ever going to get back he did not know. Increasingly he did not care.

"I mustn't lose the water hole . . . mustn't lose the water hole . . ." he muttered over and over to himself, and he leaned forward and sipped again at the water.

It tasted bad, but Sidney did not notice. Indeed, he didn't notice that he no longer even felt thirsty. Just numb: numb from the heat, the loneliness and the fear of being utterly lost.

It had been entirely his own fault, of course. The other men at the goldfield had warned him, but he had taken no notice.

"It's suicide to take a short cut across the Randalls when you don't know the country," one man had said. "Don't go Sid. Just because you've been diggin' for gold a few months you think you're an old Outback hand. Well, you're not! Follow the road!"

"Look, if I cut across country I'll save fifty miles on the journey," Sidney had replied. "I'll just go in a straight line till I get there!"

For, underneath, Sidney really *did* think that he knew all there was to know about the Outback.

"As long as I keep my eyes open I shall be all right," he said.

Carrying just a light pack he set off at a steady pace, feeling very tough, grown up and Australian. "Some of these people straight in from the towns would cart a load of gear on a walk like this one," he thought. "Or nothing at all. But not me! A bit of food, a bottle of water and a blanket—that'll do me nicely."

At first everything went well and he made good time. Then, around noon on the first day, he began to feel uneasy.

It all looked the same—that was the trouble. Very soon Sidney forgot which way he was going or which way he had come, and when he tried to retrace his steps he felt himself going giddy.

"Now wait, wait . . . I must think," he gasped. "There must be a path somewhere."

Soon he thought he had found one—animal tracks!

"Ah—these will lead across the range," he said to himself. "Some drover must have brought a herd through here. I'll be on my way safely now."

But Sidney was wrong. For, hours later, as evening was beginning to draw on, he came to the end of his trail—to find nothing but a shrivelled bush.

Suddenly he was afraid and he dashed back along the path he had followed as fast as he could. After he had been stumbling through the lengthening shadows for some time he heard something. Laughter!

"I knew I would find somebody in the end," he cried, tears of relief streaming down his cheeks. "Hello there, can you hear me? I'm coming."

The only answer was another laugh. Sidney plunged on blindly towards the noise.

Then, as the sun burnt deep red on the horizon he saw his mistake. It was no human laugh he had heard.

"A kookaburra—it's a kookaburra! Nothing but an old jacko bird . . . and I'm lost. Help me, somebody . . . help me!"

Then Sidney sank to the ground clutching his hands to his head. For he knew there was no one in that wilderness to help him.

Next day he struggled on. He lost his blanket somehow, but that didn't worry him. He drank his water, but that didn't seem to worry him either. Even the heat didn't bother him. He was in the grip of a terrible fear that left no room for any other feelings.

Towards the end of the second day he

found the water hole. At first he thought it was a mirage—like many others he had seen that day. But it was real, and he sank down by the water, utterly exhausted.

But, if there was no one to hear Sidney's cries for help there *were* people looking for him. When he did not arrive at the other side of the Randalls, the word was passed around the region to all the travellers and prospectors, cattle drovers and farmers, to keep a look out for the young city boy.

So it was that big Bill Bond, sheep shearer and drover got to hear about it: Bill Bond and Jock his dog.

Jock was Bill Bond's pride and joy, his most cherished possession. For Jock (or so Bill reckoned, and he was a rare judge of dogs) was the finest sheep-dog in Western Australia.

"You can say what you like about your collies and so forth," Bill would say, "but I think there's no finer combination for an Australian sheep-dog than you see in my Jock here—part airedale, part Irish terrier. Anyway, a good sheep-dog is born a good sheep-dog, and all the breeding in the world wont make any difference."

Nobody argued. Everyone knew that Jock was a marvellous dog with sheep—patient, fast and obedient. Besides, Bill wasn't the kind of man you argued with.

"So, this silly beggar's got himself lost has he," Bill said to his friend Charlie, another sheepshearer. "Well, I know this country and I've got an idea where he's landed himself. Jock and I will take a look: I dare say we'll find him soon enough!"

Meanwhile Sidney was desperately trying to find his own way to safety. Only now he had a second fear to fight—the fear of losing his precious water hole. So he made short explorations with the water hole as the centre. But he still found not the slightest hint of a way to safety in the shrivelled, barren scrub of the hills.

From time to time he tried crying for help again—but his voice sounded faint and distant, and increasingly he just lay hopelessly on the ground without moving.

So the hours passed and another day went by. Once Sidney thought he saw a dog, but when he blinked and looked again it was gone. "A mirage," he thought, "just a mirage." More time passed until, opening his eyes again, Sidney thought he saw the dog for the second time.

"It *is* a dog! I can really see it," he croaked and tried to rise. But he was too weak to move. So he tried to call out, but his voice was no more than a thin whisper; and when he looked again, the dog was gone.

Close by, Bill sat on his horse watching for his dog. Jock had been darting ahead and running back for some time now, and Bill had a strong feeling he knew why.

"Alive or dead, Jock's found that missing lad," he said to himself.

Just then Jock came bounding up again, barked, and then slowly started walking back the way he had come. Jock led Bill carefully across a steep ridge, down the other side, and then through a maze of piled rocks until, with a sharp bark, he brought his master to the water hole. Sidney was overcome with relief, but Bill Bond was not a man given to great displays of excitement.

"Hmm, you'll be right enough soon," was all he said. But he smiled kindly, and moved Sidney into the shadow of a rock. "We'll have a bite to eat and something hot to drink and then I'll take you back. But son, you ought never to have left the city you know!"

"I know it now," Sidney replied weakly, "and if it hadn't been for you—well, I would never have lived to go back."

"Don't thank me, lad," Bill laughed. "Thank my Jock here. The best sheep-dog in the territory he is—even when the lost sheep has only two legs and no sense at all! Now, on your feet—we've a long ride to Birkitt's Gap. You can rest there. Come on Jock! Let's be off!"

The countess, the wolf and the mastiff

Over 200 years ago, when the world was very different, the land of France was overrun with great wolves. Savage packs of wolves terrorized the whole country. Even by day, people went out into the fields only in large groups, armed as if they were going to battle. By night, few people went out at all. Many stories are still told about the dangers of those days: this one, which dates from 1764, is said to be based on events that actually happened. In those days there was one wolf in France that was feared above all others. People called him the Old Wolf, and he lived in a forest in the Auvergne country —a land of rugged hills and dense forests to this day. Old Wolf was indeed old, but he was still bigger and fiercer, stronger and wilder than any other wolf in France. He was also special in another way, for he always hunted alone, not with a pack as wolves usually do.

He was as big as a man, and had killed and eaten eighty-six people, besides wounding many others. The government of France even offered a reward to anyone who could kill or trap him, but for years no one could—in fact, quite a number of his eighty-six victims had been hunters.

As time passed, the people of the Auvergne came to think Old Wolf would never be caught, and they began to get superstitious about him.

"He is immortal, that one," somebody would say. "No man will ever kill him!"

"He's the devil himself," another would say. "He'll eat us all before long!"

But not everyone shared this view—in particular the young Countess de Mercoire. Although she had a big estate in the region she could never get any work done there, because everyone was too terrified of the wolves to go into the fields. What was more, Old Wolf had carried off many of her farm animals.

Week after week, month after month, the countess's losses mounted: sheep, lambs, goats, cattle, horses even—nothing seemed safe from Old Wolf.

The countess tried every way she knew to protect her animals and kill Old Wolf. She had traps set, ditches dug, and walls and stockades built. She had armed men mount guard over her flocks, and she sent whole armies of hunters to search the forests. But nothing worked! Old Wolf was always too clever. No trap could hold him, nor any wall or ditch keep him out. He knew all the tricks the hunters knew, and a few more besides of his own; and far from killing him, the armed guards the countess set over her animals usually ended up wounded or even dead themselves.

Finally she had a brilliant idea: she promised to marry any hunter—providing he wasn't married already, of course—who managed to catch the wolf.

Perhaps she made the offer only because she happened to be in love with a young hunter. Whatever the truth of the matter, certainly the hunter himself, whose name was Count Leonce de Verinas, was very much in love with the countess. He wasted no time at all in setting off after Old Wolf.

"After all," he thought, "I must be the first. It wouldn't do at all for the countess to marry someone else!"

Leonce set out very early one morning. To begin with he had plenty of company, for a great crowd of his friends went with him to the outskirts of the forest where the great wolf lived. However, only Leonce went on from there; the others stayed prudently behind.

But Leonce did not go quite alone: he took with him his two best friends—his dogs. There was Castor, an enormous mastiff, and Pollux, a great bloodhound. Nor, of course, did Leonce go unarmed: he took with him his heavy double-barrelled shotgun, and at his waist he wore a long-bladed hunting knife, almost as big as a short sword.

All day, Leonce and his two dogs searched for the wolf's tracks, and finally, as the afternoon was wearing on, they found them. But, of course, Old Wolf was quite as clever as he was wicked, and though neither Leonce or his dogs realised it, the great animal saw them long, long before they saw *him*. The hunter was himself being hunted!

But for many hours Old Wolf bided his time, luring Leonce, Castor and Pollux deeper and deeper into the wildest parts of the forest. Then towards evening, when Leonce was beginning to tire, Old Wolf turned on his pursuers.

Castor and Pollux stood still, their hair bristling as they sensed danger ahead. But the young hunter rushed forward into the thicket before him. He caught a glimpse of a pair of yellow eyes but, before he could even raise his gun to fire, the wolf sprang.

Old Wolf leaped on Leonce with all his weight and strength, hurling the young man to the ground and knocking him completely out. The battle seemed to be over, there and then, and yet another victim added to Old Wolf's long and terrible list, as with a growl of triumph the wolf prepared to kill his foe.

At that moment, Castor and Pollux attacked. Their master had allowed himself to be caught off guard, now it was up to the two of them to save him.

Pollux had been walking a short distance ahead of Castor, and so it was he who led the charge. Poor Pollux! He was a wonderful tracker—a true bloodhound. But like most bloodhounds, big and powerful though he was, he was also gentle at heart, and was much better at tracking than at fighting.

Now he was matched with the deadliest wolf in France . . . and his end came quickly. For Old Wolf easily dodged Pollux's attack, then swiftly caught the bloodhound by the neck and killed him with a single wrench of his terrible jaws!

That left only Castor the mastiff: but he wasn't so easy to deal with. For one thing, Castor wasn't much smaller than Old Wolf himself; and for another, he had fought many successful battles with other wolves, and was not afraid of them.

So the battle raged, to and fro, across and around and about Leonce's fallen body—Castor the mastiff defending his master because he loved him; Old Wolf hating man and dog, in the same way as he hated everything that lived.

Time after time Castor attacked. He tried every trick he had ever learned, and he used every bit of courage and strength he had. But neither skill nor courage seemed to be enough! Castor could have escaped himself, for Old Wolf was intent on killing the insolent young hunter who had dared invade his territory. But Castor did not think of escape at all. For he meant to rescue his young master, and he knew that somehow he had to drive the great wolf away.

The two animals rolled over in the dust, raising a choking cloud as they bit and scratched and tore at each other. But every time the result was the same: Old Wolf flung back Castor, and forced him to retreat. Then, with a growl of triumph, the great wolf would turn towards Leonce and prepare to kill him.

Again and again, tired, bloody and bruised, Castor would attack, desperately flinging himself on his enemy.

At last the brave dog had the strength for only one last effort. He was bleeding heavily, but he knew that unless he drove the wolf off this time or killed him, Leonce his master was done for. He attacked!

As he did so, Leonce began to revive. Painfully he opened his eyes. He was still dazed, and for a moment could not remember where he was or what he was doing there, let alone what was happening. All around there was dust and noise—howling and barking—and Leonce was wet with blood: the blood of dog and wolf who had been fighting for so long over his fallen body.

Then his mind cleared—and just in time too, for at that very moment Old Wolf planted both his front feet on Leonce's chest as he drove back the last despairing attack of the brave mastiff.

"It's time I did something useful," Leonce muttered to himself. "It is my fault for running ahead too fast. Now I must help!"

With that the young man stretched out his hand for his gun—but it was far out of his reach and he knew without trying that he did not have the strength to push Old Wolf off him so that he could get up and reach it.

"I've only one chance left!" Leonce gasped, quickly pulling his long hunting knife from its sheath in his belt.

Old Wolf's two hind legs were on Leonce now, his two forefeet being wrapped round Castor's head while the animals struggled to bite each other. Leonce paused for just a moment—Old Wolf's shaggy chest was right above his face—then thrust the long sharp knife upwards as hard as he could, deep, deep into the wolf's cruel heart.

Old Wolf gave a last wild scream, full of hate, then crashed down, right on top of Leonce, almost crushing him.

So it was that Castor the mastiff saved his master, and helped him kill the Old Wolf of the Auvergne—to win both the government's reward and the hand of the Countess de Mercoire.

Not surprisingly, when the Countess and Leonce were married soon afterwards, the guest of honour was neither a local nobleman nor one of the bride's or groom's family. It was Castor the mastiff, of course!

The beggar's dog

Laws are meant to protect, and the laws that most countries have requiring dogs to be licensed are no exception. They are intended to ensure that only people who really want dogs, and will care for them properly, will keep them. Yet there are many examples on record of the accidental cruelties that were caused by the introduction of dog licences; cruelties usually to the very poorest people, who had no money to spare.

This is the story of just such a case which happened long ago in Germany. It is based on a poem by Albert von Chamisso, a Frenchman who spent much of his life in Berlin, where he was a professor of botany. The beggar in the poem was an old man who had never, even in his best days, been very fortunate. Now it seemed he was sinking a little lower every day. His clothes were in tatters, his pockets were empty, and no one would give him work; and he was old and tired. In all the world he had only one possession, one friend, and one comfort; and all three were one and the same: his dog Pompey.

Pompey was a rather undersized—and definitely underfed—little black-and-white terrier, given to swift movements and sharp, loud barking. Like his master, Pompey was growing old.

He had been the weakest of the litter, and the beggar had got him for nothing from the man who had been on the way to drown him. It had meant nothing to the man—what was one miserable puppy more or less anyway? But to the beggar the tiny defenceless ball of warm fur he had taken into his hand had been the most beautiful thing he had ever seen or ever held.

Since that day the beggar had lavished on Pompey all those feelings that people usually divide between their families and their closest, dearest friends. For, in a life as bleak, hard and hopeless as his, the beggar seldom had any feelings left over to give to anyone else. All he had, he needed for himself alone: pity, bitterness, fear, rage.

But the poor little terrier became wife and children, family and friends all rolled into one, and with him for company the gloom of the beggar's life never seemed quite so bad again.

Wherever the beggar went Pompey went too. In summer he shared the heat and dust; in winter the cold and wet. He never once complained and never failed to cheer his master when he saw care weighing him down more than usual.

Together they begged in the streets and markets; together they slept under hedges and on park benches, sheltered in doorways, fled from the heavy tread of the policeman on his beat.

It so happened that things were at their very worst for the beggar and Pompey when the new dog licence law was passed.

"A dog licence! Where on earth am I going to find the money for a dog licence?" the poor man grumbled up into the policeman's red face.

"That's your problem, old man, not mine," said the policeman with a cruel laugh.

The beggar cursed: "My problem, I'll say it's my problem," he muttered. "Where am I going to get three marks from?"

The policeman still stood laughing, then the beggar cried out again: "What will happen if I don't pay, eh? Tell me that!"

"If you don't pay? Well now, that will be breaking the law that will," the policeman answered smugly. "If you don't pay then your dog will be considered a stray—and will be taken from you forthwith to an appointed place where it will be detained (I quote from the regulations) and, to cut a long story short, done away with! Killed! Understand?"

The policeman turned on his heel and walked quickly away. The beggar squatted on his haunches beside his dog.

"Little Pompey, my friend, what are we to do? What am *I* to do?"

Pompey gave a soft whine and nuzzled the old man's hand. He had never seen his master so depressed, even in his worst misery. He did his best to comfort him.

The beggar sat slumped in thought. He was turning over in his mind everything that had happened to him since the day he had saved Pompey from drowning, trying to imagine what life would have been like had Pompey not been there to share with him.

"Who pitied me when I lost the last of my money?" he thought. "Pompey, that's who! Not my family, oh no! The moment my business failed and I couldn't pay my debts they disowned me. How many times did I give money to that brother of mine? Yet when I needed money to save myself he didn't offer me a penny in return. Not a penny, no! Did he even offer to lend me so much as the price of a meal? No!

"But you Pompey, you didn't complain when I had to stop buying you meat and good bones, nor even when there wasn't so much as a crust of bread to eat. You didn't leave me when I had to move out of my house into dirty lodgings, and from the lodgings into the street. Ah, if that wife of mine had shown such loyalty, perhaps I wouldn't be in the gutter now. But no, my brother and wife were *people*, and people put themselves first—*always*. But you are a dog, and you took the stale bread I gave you, and the dirty cold lodgings and the dirtier, colder streets—just to be with me."

Again Pompey looked up into the old beggar's faded blue eyes and did his best to comfort him. He licked the thin hands and the careworn face, and tried with all his heart to make the man understand.

"I know, master dear," he wanted to say. "I know. Don't reproach yourself. I am happy just being with you. Don't worry about the past, and don't worry about the future either. The police? Bah! What sort of a terrier do you take me for if you think I can't keep out of their way?"

But it was no good. Try as he might, little Pompey could not speak, and his master's depression seemed to be beyond his powers to lift.

"I was sick and they ignored me—all of them!" the beggar muttered furiously to himself. "All of them, except my Pompey! They turned me from their doors they did, me, whom they had known for years. But Pompey stuck with me, of yes! Through thick and thin! Why, that night when I nearly died of cold after I couldn't beg an overcoat at the market—he crept inside my jacket and kept me alive with his own warmth!"

"Yes, yes, master, I did," sighed Pompey. "What else should a dog—any dog—do? Didn't you keep me alive when the man would have drowned me?"

"But come now, there have been better times too. Remember last summer when we got work guarding the haberdasher's stall in the market when he went off for his lunch? What a meal we ate that night under the trees! Remember the time the steaks fell off the butcher's cart and I carried them home to you? No, it hasn't all been bad, and it may get better again."

But the beggar was too busy with the bad memories to spare time for the good, though there were certainly not many good things to remember.

Then, with sudden energy, the old man scrambled to his feet.

"Three marks! three marks! How can I find it? I can't! But I won't let them take you, Pompey, and I won't let you starve in misery with me any longer. Come!"

Then he walked off as fast as his sore feet and broken shoes would allow, holding Pompey's string lead firmly in his hand.

Soon they were standing on the banks of the great, swift, grey river, swollen and fat with winter rain.

"I saved you once from drowning," said the old man, "but for whose benefit? For yours? To give you the honour of starving to death with me? No, for mine! Because I was selfish and lonely! It wasn't enough for me that *I* had to be miserable. I had to have a fellow creature alongside me to share my misery! I'm as bad as all the rest, thinking only of myself. But now I must think of you. You have a right to be free of this misery, and you shall be free, in just a moment. You shall be free, and no hand but mine has the right to do it!"

Quickly the beggar tied the spare end of his dog's string lead around a heavy stone lying by the riverside.

"Come, my poor Pompey, don't look at me. It will be over quickly. I can be selfish no longer. I must face what remains of my life alone!"

As he raised the stone above his head, for the last time Pompey lifted himself on his hind legs and looked into his master's face.

Then suddenly, as in a blinding flash, the beggar saw the truth of all things very, very clearly. All his self pity and selfishness fell away, and he gasped:

"Set you free, yes—I will, I must! But not this way. How strange that even at the last I should have found so many excellent reasons and so many fine words for doing myself a good turn!"

With a quick twist of his hand, the beggar loosened the lead around Pompey's neck and, quickly, tied it around his own. Then, without looking back or saying a word more, he threw himself into the deep, dark, fast-flowing water.

Despairingly, Pompey leaped into the water after him. For some minutes the little dog desperately splashed about in the water over the spot where his master had gone in. All the time he howled and whined, making such a noise that at last some sailors from a boat moored nearby came running along the bank to see what was the matter with him.

"There's someone in there, someone in the water!" came the cry, and while one man pulled off his heavy sea boots and plunged directly into the river, others raced back to launch a small boat which they rowed to the spot.

They found Pompey's master—oh yes. But alas, they did not find him in time. He was drowned.

His had been a bitter life, and a wasted one. Some might say a pointless one too, though Pompey would never have agreed to that. Pompey the terrier did not share Man's own opinion of himself: that it was necessary, or at least desirable, to do something and succeed in something in life.

To Pompey life was simply *life*. Success or failure did not matter at all. You lived as well as you could, and that was that.

The sailors collected enough money among themselves to pay for a funeral, and when the old beggar was laid to rest, his little dog stretched himself upon the new grave and cried like an orphan child: cried and cried until, exhausted at last, he died.

Shippeitaro and the samurai

The Japanese have many marvellous stories about dogs, for whom they have always had a deep affection and respect. This story is probably at least 2,000 years old.

Once long, long ago in old Japan, a samurai was travelling through a strange province. He found it necessary to cross some rugged mountains and, as luck would have it, he had not gone very far when darkness began to fall.

"It would be most unwise to spend the night in the open here," he thought to himself. "There's danger about; lions or wolves or worse—and I wouldn't like to have to meet them in the dark and in the open."

So he hastened along as fast as he could until, in the last rays of the setting sun, he saw a tumbledown temple standing before him.

It wasn't much, but it was better than nothing. Its columns had crumbled, its roof had long since collapsed, and its floors were overgrown with grass and weeds.

"What sort of temple can this have been?" wondered the samurai. "Plainly it hasn't been used in a hundred years."

He climbed up a ruined buttress, backed up against one of the few walls still standing more or less whole, spread his blanket, and tried to make himself comfortable.

"At least this way I'm off the ground and protected from the rear," thought the samurai.

Then he drew his sword, lay down with it in his hand, covered himself first with his blanket then his shield, and tried to sleep.

At first he did sleep, for he was very, very tired and not inclined to be nervous anyway.

But then, just before midnight, he was awakened by a dreadful, unearthly howling noise. He started up in fear, and a cold sweat was on him. What on earth could it be?

"Lucky for me I came up here," he thought, for all the noise was coming from below him. Cautiously he peeped over the edge of the parapet and looked down. The moon was shining brightly and he could see very clearly.

There below him were cats. *Cats*. Hundreds of cats, of all shapes, colours, and sizes, all howling and screaming in a blood-curdling manner. Indeed, they seemed to be actually singing or saying something.

The samurai strained to understand, and after a time he thought he could recognize a single phrase, repeated over and over again: "Tell it not to Shippeitaro . . . Tell it not to Shippeitaro . . . Tell it not to Shippeitaro!"

"Who or what can Shippeitaro mean—or be?" wondered the samurai.

Then suddenly the cats turned tail and vanished into the night shadows, so suddenly that it seemed they had disappeared into thin air.

"Even as a dream such a sight as this would seem fantastic," thought the samurai, smiling in spite of everything. "Still, dream-

ing is something I've got to find time for. I have a feeling I'm going to be glad of a good sleep before this adventure is over."

So he slept again. Peacefully, though with his sword in his hand as before.

In the morning he left the temple and continued on his way. But whereas before he had been anxious to cross the mountains as quickly as possible, now he was very anxious to find out more about the temple and the cats.

He didn't have long to wait!

Very shortly he came in sight of a small village. On its outskirts was a house rather larger and more solidly built than the rest—a village hall it seemed. From it came sounds of great lamentations—sobs, cries of despair, moans and piteous groans.

"What on earth can be the meaning of this?" the samurai asked himself.

He knocked on the door and entered. The room was full of people, weeping and tearing their hair and beating their breasts in sorrow. It looked like every funeral since the world began, squeezed together into one small space.

"What is the matter, good people?" cried the samurai. "Why these lamentations? Come, tell me. What great sorrow or affliction has come upon you? Tell me, so that I—one of the Emperor's samurai may help!"

The crying died away almost to nothing, except for a few dry sobs. For a moment the red-eyed people in the room stared at him, then they came thronging around him.

"Help us—oh yes, you must! Please!"

"Our prayers are answered!"

"But what can one man do, or any man?" So went the babble of voices.

"Wait, wait, slowly," pleaded the samurai. "Tell me the trouble, at least."

"Alas, noble samurai," said an old man pushing his way to the front of the crowd, "we have only too good a reason for tears. For tonight we shall lose the fairest maiden in our village. The spirit of the mountain will take her and eat her. We are powerless."

"Just a minute," cried the samurai. "Has this anything to do with the ruined temple up in the mountains—for I spent the night there."

"You have spent the night there? Then already you have proved your courage—and your luck, which is worth more than courage when you are dealing with evil spirits," the old man said with respect in his voice. "Did you by any chance see anything of—of *cats*?"

"Indeed I did," said the samurai, "and very puzzling it all was. But tell me more about this evil spirit."

"Well sir, tonight we must take the maiden to the temple where you spent the night. We must take her in a cage. In the morning the mountain spirit will eat her. It is the same every year—we lose a girl in the same way, and no one will help us."

"Oh but this year someone will," laughed the samurai. "Mountain spirits don't worry me as much as they do you—they looked like cats to me, and if the temple has nothing worse to offer I'll save your girl and rid you of this curse for ever! Tell me," he said, "what is Shippeitaro?"

"Shippeitaro is a dog," answered a woman with a tear-stained face, whom the samurai guessed to be the mother of the girl due to be sacrificed. "Yes, a fine dog too. He is brave and strong, yet gentle with children—he belongs to the head man of our prince."

"Does he indeed!" exclaimed the samurai. "Well, somehow or other he is going to play an important role in whatever I do, so where can I find him?"

The woman explained, and the samurai strode off as fast as he could. As he walked he heard the weeping begin again—obviously the girl's family feared he meant to run away, and that their daughter was still going to be eaten by the mountain spirit.

But the samurai had quite different plans. An hour later he returned, leading the dog Shippeitaro on a lead of plaited leather.

Shippeitaro was a golden colour, with a purple tongue—we would call him a chow.

The prince's head man had not minded at all when the samurai had asked to borrow his dog for a time, and now the samurai and Shippeitaro were firm friends.

Back at the house, the cage—large, with close-set bars, and curtained inside with red silk— was ready, and the poor, terrified girl was about to step into it.

"You can forget that," snapped the samurai. "The girl stays here! That spirit, if spirit he is, has eaten his last village maiden—though if things go wrong he may be about to eat his first samurai! Still, with luck and courage as you say—and skill too—I shall prove a dish not at all to his taste!"

Then the samurai put Shippeitaro into the cage in the girl's place and locked it up.

"Now, I am going with you when you take this cage up the mountain," he said. "Then we shall see what we shall see."

Soon they all set off: the samurai and four young men carrying the cage. When they arrived at the ruined temple the samurai begged the young men to stay with him.

"Come, come, you all have stout cudgels and knives," he cried with indignation. "Stay and fight! I tell you the mountain spirit is not as dreadful as you fear. Stay and fight!"

But it was no good. The young men were terrified, and rushed back down the mountain so fast that some forgot their legs and rolled most of the way head-over-heels.

"Oh well," said the samurai, rapping gently on the bars of the cage with his knuckles. "It seems we alone are to face the spirit of the mountain—how do you feel Shippeitaro, old soldier?"

Shippeitaro gave an encouraging growl, then barked and (though the samurai couldn't see him) wagged his tail. Obviously there was no fear there!

Night fell, and very soon the dreadful howls of the cats began to ring out once again on the silent mountain.

The samurai had had the cage placed at the foot of the old buttress where he had slept the night before. From above, he could lean over the edge and reach the lock of the cage door. Everything was ready.

Midnight came and the howling of the cats rose to a terrible crescendo. Carefully the samurai looked over the top of the buttress—and gasped. For even he was unprepared for what he saw now. The cats were dancing in a frenzied ring, and in the centre of them was the biggest tomcat that ever lived. He was black with eyes like coals of fire, and his tail swished and lashed to and fro. Round and round he danced, until he was only a few yards from the cage. The samurai could see his sharp teeth glittering as he licked his lips at the thought of the meal he imagined he was about to have.

"Luck, courage, skill—let's hope Shippeitaro and I both have them," muttered the samurai, and with a quick movement he leaned over the edge of the buttress and undid the lock on the cage.

There was a crash as Shippeitaro beat the door open in his impatience to be out, and a sudden flash of gold as the gallant dog shot out like an arrow from a bow, and grabbed the great tomcat firmly in his jaws. Then down leaped the samurai and with a great cry, swept the giant tomcat's head from its shoulders with one mighty swing of his two-handed sword.

The other cats were so astonished they forgot to run away, and Shippeitaro soon put an end to them.

Hours later the men and women in the little house were suddenly aroused by a fierce knock on the door. They leaped up aghast, but then their fear turned to joy, for they heard a great joyous bark from Shippeitaro and a shout of victory from the samurai.

Then indeed all their tears were forgotten and praise and thanksgiving were universal—the greatest praise of all going to Shippeitaro, the bravest dog in all Japan.

Buddy the seeing eye

If you had been walking along New York's West Street one day in 1928, you might have seen something quite extraordinary: a man crossing the road.

Perhaps this seems a very commonplace occurrence to you, and so it is, even if West Street in 1928 was no ordinary street. It flanked the dock area of the great city, and along it thousands of cars, lorries, carts, motor cycles, barrows and trolleys were driven, pushed and pulled at all hours of the day and night, and at the fastest possible speed. Nowhere in all its length was there so much as a single traffic light, and the chaos and confusion were like nothing else in the whole of the great city.

Even so, what was so special about one man crossing a road, even a busy one like West Street? The man had a dog with him, and in fact it was the dog who led the way through the bustling traffic. For the man was blind, and his dog was none other than the first trained "Seeing Eye" guide dog to appear in the United States.

Of course, there had been guide dogs before then. But never had anyone properly trained dog and man to work together, not with one leading and the other following, but as a team, working so much in unison that to an onlooker they appeared to think and move almost as one.

The man's name was Frank Morris, the dog's Buddy. Buddy was an alsatian bitch, despite her boyish-sounding name. She had been specially bred in Switzerland for guide-dog work, and it was Frank who had decided to call her Buddy—for her original name had been Kiss.

Buddy and Frank had been brought together through an article in a magazine, describing how in Germany dogs were being specially trained as guides for blinded ex-soldiers.

The author of the article was Dorothy Eustis, herself an American, who lived in Switzerland where she bred and trained dogs for all kinds of special police and army work. Now she was interested in the idea of guide dogs for the blind. Slowly she began to work out the details of her scheme. This meant breeding the right kind of dogs, and finding dedicated help in order to turn a good idea into a great reality. She called her scheme the Seeing Eye.

That magazine article was the turning point of all her work; hearing about it was the most important thing that ever happened to Frank Morris. He was so overwhelmed by the whole idea that he immediately wrote to Dorothy to ask if there really were dogs of the sort she had written about, dogs who could set him free from the prison of helpless blindness he hated so much, free to go where-ever he wanted like a seeing person.

Were there any dogs like that? Certainly there were. In Mrs. Eustis's own kennels. But, Dorothy Eustis wrote to him, dog and man had to be trained together. He would have to come to Switzerland. Would he be willing to do that?

Frank's home was in Nashville, Tenessee. He was nineteen and had been blind all his life. There was every kind of risk: Frank would have to go alone; how would he manage on the journey? Supposing it didn't work!

Frank made up his mind. He *had* to go! So he set out, first for New York, then for Paris, and finally for the little town of Vevey in Switzerland.

His journey had in it everything that blind people—blind people without Seeing Eye guide dogs, that is—fear and hate.

There was the terrible bustle of New York, followed by the loneliness of the voyage across. The people on the ship led him from one "safe" place—the dining-room, a deck chair, his own cabin—to another, in the hope that he would stay safely in one spot without moving until it was time for him to go to sleep. Even when he was in bed they locked his cabin door!

In Paris Frank had his worst time yet: he did not speak a word of French and no one, it seemed, spoke a word of English. So he never once left his hotel room until he was led to the train for Switzerland and began the final stage of his journey.

While all these things were happening to Frank the people at Vevey were busy on their own account, making ready for this most important arrival. They had enormous experience of breeding and training dogs for all sorts of work, but not as guide dogs for the blind. This required a very special kind of training. Complete obedience and brilliant guiding skill were only part of what was needed. More important than anything else, the dogs had to learn to think for their master as well as just to see for him. Not all dogs could be taught these skills, not even all the carefully bred female alsatians that the trainers of the Seeing Eye found to be the most suitable type for the job.

The training, even in its earliest stages, took at least two hours a day. The dogs had to be taught how to walk, how to cross roads, how to go up and down stairs and mount kerbs, how to negotiate crowds and traffic—doing these things not as a dog would do them, but as a person would. They had to learn how to warn their master of an obstacle in his path, and how to change direction without tripping him over.

At last, soon after Frank's arrival, a dog was selected to be his.

Her name was Kiss (at least, it was until Frank changed it). She was a beautiful dark grey colour, intelligent and quick to learn; but above all, she was gentle and very understanding, for Frank Morris needed to find love as well as help from his Seeing Eye dog.

Buddy and Frank quickly became devoted to one another, but it needed many weeks of training before the partnership—which was to be so important to thousands of sightless people all over the world—was perfect. It was not simply a matter of training Buddy, but of training Buddy and Frank together, until—together—they could face all the problems and obstacles of modern life. They had to be trained to cope with life not in a safe, familiar house, or hospital, or some quiet country village, but in bustling modern towns and crowded cities.

At last the great day came when it was time for Frank and Buddy to make their first trip into Vevey together. Down the path they went to the cable car which led from the steep hill overlooking the blue lake to the town below: the town with its busy streets, its traffic, and its people.

Frank still shuffled along at his slow "blindman's pace"; Buddy on the other hand walked smoothly and effortlessly. By the time they stopped for a drink in a café, Frank was exhausted. He had only walked a mile, but he wasn't used to so much exercise. Blind people without dogs never have much chance to go for long walks!

In the days that followed the walks became longer and longer; and every day brought new problems to be faced and overcome.

All this was part of the programme, but one day something happened which was part of no plan, and which came near to bringing all progress to a tragic stop. As it was, the incident merely showed Buddy's qualities, and how close she and Frank had become.

This is what happened. One afternoon, after one of their expeditions into Vevey, Buddy and Frank were walking back home from the cable car station. With them was Jack Humphrey, one of the trainers at the Seeing Eye.

Suddenly they heard the clatter of hooves, the rumble of cartwheels, and the neigh of frantic horses. Then round a bend in the road came a runaway waggon, the horses completely out of control.

The wagon filled the whole road. Their only escape lay in climbing the steep earth embankment beside the road.

Desperately Jack Humphrey looked around. What could he do? The embankment was as high as a man: he himself could climb it, but what could he do for Frank? Frank was a big man; blind, helpless . . . if Jack tried to help him they would both be killed. But how could Jack abandon him in his danger? What *could* he do?

Luckily for them all, there was somebody else at hand who made up her mind in an instant: Buddy.

Now Buddy could have saved herself alone if she had wanted to, simply by ripping herself away from Frank's grasp and outrunning the cart. But no such thought entered her head. Instinctively she thought for both of them, and in doing so saved them all and proved herself a truly perfect guide dog.

In a flash she pulled Frank to the embankment and, despite his weight and lack of help (poor Frank didn't understand what was happening), not only struggled to the top, but hauled her blind master after her. It was an incredible feat of strength, and when Jack Humphrey himself clambered to safety it was to find that—thanks to Buddy—Frank had beaten him to it.

Now there could be no doubt that the training was complete. Only one problem remained, and that was in Frank's mind. But this problem too was solved, one day soon after the incident with the waggon.

"Mrs. Eustis, will you get someone to take me into town?" Frank asked. "I need a haircut."

"Why should anyone take you?" replied Mrs. Eustis. "Go yourself."

In an instant Frank realized that for the first time in his whole life he was free: free to go where he liked when he liked, free to walk, free to go out, free to travel. He was a person, not just a problem to the world and to himself.

Frank's return journey to the United States was nothing like his trip out, even if he did go by exactly the same route. This time he didn't just go through Paris, he explored it. This time no one locked him in his cabin on the ship. Finally he reached America, and so our story comes full circle, to that scene in New York's chaotic West Street where it began.

In 1929 Mrs. Eustis herself returned to the USA and the Seeing Eye was established there. Quickly it spread to more countries, changing the lives of thousands of blind people wherever it was established. Pioneers as they were, Frank Morris and Buddy his dog had helped to make history.

The memoirs of Gengisk

Frederick the Great of Prussia, who lived from 1712 to 1786, has left behind a legendary reputation as one of the greatest of European kings and soldiers. Throughout his long life he kept many pets—indeed some people have said that he preferred dogs to people! Certainly Gengisk, who tells this story, was a great favourite and accompanied Frederick on many of his campaigns. His memorial can still be seen in Frederick's great palace of Sans Souci at Potsdam.

The events he describes are believed to have actually happened, though some people think other dogs, not Gengisk, may have been involved in them. Here, at any rate, is Gengisk's story.

I have so many memories, for I have lived through some very exciting times. So many wars, so many battles; so many different allies and enemies; so many generals; so many victories, so many defeats.

Of course, we court dogs have the best of it. Life isn't much fun for the poor devils of soldiers on any side. Funny sort of creatures, men! I've seen all sorts, from the best to the worst, but I still wouldn't claim to understand them. Why, I wouldn't claim even to understand my dear master, Frederick. He's one of the best—at least as far as we dogs are concerned. He is also one of the most important people in the world. Frederick the Great they call him: King of Prussia.

Our home is in Potsdam, which is a fine city I can tell you, though if you ask me, a home should be the place where you spend most time. We have been on so many campaigns and lived in so many nasty, cold, unhealthy camps that I almost feel like a stranger inside four walls.

But there! I've forgotten to introduce myself. I'm Gengisk, a dog. I guess you would call me a great dane, though we dogs don't set much store by those funny titles you people give us. As far as we are concerned we are dogs: big or small, smooth-haired or rough, long-haired or short; all dogs, but all different. Mind you, we do all speak the same language, unlike you people now—and I think we are better off for it. Did you ever hear of a war between dogs? Certainly not! It's quite unthinkable. But there, you see, we can always understand what we say to each other, not like you humans.

But to get back to my story, I've been with

Frederick since I was a puppy. I'm not his only dog by any means—he is very fond of dogs. "The more I see of men, the more I like my dogs," is what he said once, so that just shows you. Anyway, the palace is full of us. There's me and any number of those smallish Italian greyhounds, and there was a terrier too, but I'll get to him later.

Well now, when I was a bit younger I always went with Frederick on his campaigns. It was a very exciting life up to a point. The trouble with war, from my experience anyway, is that it goes on and on, even when everyone is totally tired of it. You human beings never know when to stop.

Take the time I'm thinking of now. Frederick was always a great one for riding out to see a situation for himself. A dangerous thing to do in the middle of a battle, of course, but on the occasion I am talking about he was well inside our lines and things were very quiet. On the other hand, he went out entirely alone—leaving even me behind.

I settled down in his tent for a sleep, but suddenly I awoke with this very strong feeling of danger. It may be difficult for you to understand—you people call it a "sixth sense"—but although I couldn't see or hear or smell anything wrong, I *felt* the danger and felt it getting stronger every minute.

"The enemy must have broken through," I thought, "or sent out a raiding party."

Obviously there wasn't a moment to lose. I chased off after the king as fast as I could. Luckily his horse was just trotting, and I was able to take a short cut or two that a man on a horse couldn't use. Soon I had him in sight. He heard me coming and reined in, but he would have gone on again if I hadn't managed to stop him.

That was the difficult part, for kings are used to doing just what they want, *when* they want, and even a favourite dog finds it difficult to make one change his mind. What I did was this: I jumped up at his saddle and pulled at his boot—which at first he thought was a great joke, and then he thought it was a nuisance. Then I started snapping at the horse's reins and bridle. Frederick still didn't get the point, though by now I could actually hear the danger as well as sense it.

Finally, I just stood in the way and wouldn't let his horse pass. That did it!

He dismounted. I whipped around and took an on-guard position, facing the direction the danger was coming from. At last Frederick heard it for himself.

Horses. Horses approaching quickly but carefully; running not on the road but on the grass verge—a thing that our Prussian cavalry certainly wouldn't bother to do, behind our own lines as we were. He moved quickly then all right. He gave his horse a wallop on the rump that sent him cantering off home, and then he and I tore off and hid under a little wooden bridge over a drainage ditch. Not a moment too soon, either. Dear me, I can remember the riders so clearly: Russian Cossacks with shaved heads, swords, lances and high leather boots.

They went thundering over the bridge and on out of sight. After a few minutes I crept out and scouted around. They had gone, so Frederick and I went back to camp as fast as we could—though not by the road—and we took good care to keep under cover the whole way.

Well, the next exciting thing that I can remember happening involved the Russians again, and a Polish general of theirs called Nadasti. It was after one of our less successful battles (at a place called Soor if you want to know). Nobody can win all the time and Frederick and his generals were no exception. As I say, things went badly wrong; the Russians threw in a surprise attack and captured a part of our camp, a part which unfortunately included His Majesty's carriages and me. I had stayed to guard them you see, and before I knew what was happening I was surrounded

They treated me very kindly, I'll say that for them, and I'll say something else too: there were plenty on our side who were none too sorry at the outcome. I mean, who were glad that I was bagged. Some were dogs who thought that without me they'd have things all their own way, and some were men who were jealous (can you believe it?) of the amount of attention I got.

What happened to me? I was passed on by the general to his wife. She looked after me very well indeed, first while the war dragged on, then while peace negotiations dragged on even more.

Every day I used to watch the messengers arrive, and then scan Madame Nadasti's face to see if there was any news concerning the peace treaty and me. You see, for all her kindnesses, being with her wasn't the same as being at home with Frederick, and she knew it. But at last it was all arranged. A special clause was put into the treaty about me: I was to be handed back to the Prussians immediately.

Of all my memories, none comes to me across the years so vividly as that reunion. I was led to Frederick's tent and the guard lifted the flap for me. His Majesty was sitting with his back to the entrance, so he didn't see me come in. I'm afraid I couldn't keep control of myself. I jumped up on his desk. Imagine it! I'm not a small dog by any standards! Well, the map went one way, the commander-in-chief's despatch went another, the quartermaster-general's report went a third, and all the other things on the desk—and Frederick himself, I may say—were thrown into confusion. Luckily I had my feet on the king's shoulders or else he might have fallen over altogether. But the moment he saw who it was he joined in with the same spirit.

Ah, that was marvellous, marvellous! The best time of my whole life.

Rather less pleasant was the discovery that, while I had been away, another dog—a wretched little white terrier—had become something of a favourite. Not that Frederick preferred him to me, of course, but he needed company and had granted the terrier a favoured position among his dogs. The terrier, being the sort he was, took advantage of it.

Dear, dear, it still makes me boil with rage. He really thought he was important, that little fellow, and he couldn't abide my coming home.

I had nothing against *him*—don't get me wrong—but he couldn't let a moment pass without playing some nasty trick: overturning my water bowl, tipping my plate of bones on the floor, teasing me whenever he could. Why, when Frederick wasn't in the room he even took to giving me little bites on the ears or tail or foot.

The impudence of that terrier! Why, if it hadn't been for the fact that I was ten times his size I would have bitten his head off.

But I got my revenge—oh yes. I waited until we were in our winter camp on the Danube. The river was in flood: lots of water and plenty of débris floating in it, bits of tree, that sort of thing.

The terrier started playing me up, as usual, but this time I didn't let it go. I just picked him up in my mouth by the scruff of the neck—it didn't hurt him—and carefully swam right across that racing river to the other side. There I put him down, gave him a nod, then swam back to my own side. How the soldiers laughed! He looked really ridiculous. You see, he was afraid to risk swimming the river, and he was afraid and angry and ashamed of himself all at the same time. He hung around for a bit and then slunk off. I don't know where he went, but he never came back to camp.

Well, I think I've told you enough of my adventures for now. Age is catching me up and I'm beginning to feel a little tired. I haven't really done much exciting lately, living with King Frederick at Sans Souci palace. Recently I've been ill a couple of times, and the king has looked after me himself, night and day. He's very good to me and I'm happy here. Plenty of food, the best of masters, and all my memories.

The dogs of the tinderbox

Stories of magical dogs are found all over the world. This one, from Denmark, was written by Hans Christian Andersen.

To anyone else the countryside might have seemed rather bleak, and the road lonely, but to the soldier returning safely from the wars it had all the charm that absence of danger gives to someone who is only too used to it.

The soldier was walking quietly along thinking about this when, suddenly rounding a bend, he found himself face to face with an old woman. He had no doubt at all that she was a witch.

"You're a fine-looking fellow if ever I saw one," she cackled. "How would you like to have as much money as you can carry?"

"I would like that very much," the soldier answered, "but how do I go about it?"

"Easy," said the witch. "Do you see that hollow tree over there just by the road? Well if you climb to the top you will find you can get right down inside it. I'll tie a rope around your waist to pull you back again. When you get to the bottom you will find yourself in a wide, well-lit passage. Go along it. Then you will see three doors with keys in the locks—open them and go in. Inside the first room you will find a large wooden chest with a dog sitting on it—no ordinary dog, mark you, for his eyes are as large as saucers. But you need not be afraid of him. I'll lend you my blue apron: all you have to do is spread it on the floor and then boldly pick him up and sit him down on it. He won't move a muscle after that. Then you can go to the chest and take whatever you want. It's full of copper coins.

"Inside the second chamber is another chest and another dog—only this time his eyes are the size of mill-wheels and the chest contains silver coins. The third chamber has a chest stuffed full of gold—and a dog with eyes the size of the Round Tower. But in either case you only have to spread my blue apron on the floor and boldly pick the dog up and set him down on it for everything to be safe and easy."

"This sounds almost too good to be true," said the soldier, "but one thing puzzles me: What do you hope to get out of it?"

"No money—you can be sure of that," said the witch. "The only thing I want is for you to bring back an old tinderbox my grandmother left in the passage the last time she was down there."

"In that case, where's the rope?" laughed the soldier. "For I can't wait to get my hands on all that money."

In a moment he was inside the tree and

into the passage, which was brightly lit by dozens of lamps. Before him, just as the witch had said, he saw three doors.

Boldly he turned the key in the lock of the first, and entered. There indeed stood the chest, and on top of it the biggest dog the soldier had ever seen, with eyes exactly the size of saucers!

Quickly the soldier spread the apron on the ground, then seized the great hound and set him down on it. The dog seemed not to take any interest in him whatever, and the soldier had all the time he needed to open the chest and stuff his pockets with copper coins.

After that the soldier went to the next room, where an even larger dog was guarding the treasure: a dog with eyes the size of mill-wheels.

Once again the soldier spread the blue apron and seized the enormous beast without fear, and once again the animal took no interest in what went on. This time however the chest was full of silver, and the soldier filled his pockets, first throwing away the copper coins he had already taken.

But the third chamber surpassed everything. In it the dog was the biggest animal of any sort the soldier had ever seen, with eyes that were truly the size of the Round Tower. But for all that the animal remained perfectly calm when the soldier seated him on the blue apron and opened the chest.

"Good heavens!" the soldier gasped, for the chest was full to the brim with shiny gold coins. "There's enough here to buy all Copenhagen!" And he lost no time in emptying his pockets of the silver and refilling them with gold.

Then he replaced the enormous hound, closed the door behind him, picked up the witch's tinderbox, and in a minute or so was back on the ground outside the tree.

"Tell me one thing," asked the soldier, "what exactly do you want the tinderbox for? It must be very important."

"That's no business of yours," snapped the witch. "Give me the tinderbox at once!"

"Now then," said the soldier, getting angry. "Either you tell me or I cut off your head. Which is it to be?"

"I won't tell you!" screamed the witch.

So the soldier drew his sword and, true to his word, cut off her head at a stroke. Then he knotted up all the gold in her blue apron, put the tinderbox in his pocket, and set off for the nearest town.

There he took expensive lodgings, bought himself a whole wardrobe full of the finest clothes, spent his time at theatres, balls, and parties, and generally passed himself off as a very great and rich man. In fact, he did everything he wanted—everything, that is, except one thing. The king of the city had a beautiful daughter whom he kept locked up and closely guarded, because it had once been predicted that one day she would marry a common soldier. Of course our soldier very much wanted to meet her, but despite all his efforts he failed to arrange it.

Then one day he had to stop thinking about the princess, for he realized to his horror that he had spent nearly all the money he had brought from the tree.

So he went to live in a tiny attic at the top of a dark old house, and sold all his fine clothes. The day came at last when he had no money at all. It was then that he remembered the tinderbox.

"Let's see if I can get a spark of light from it at least," he said.

No sooner had he rubbed the flint against the steel than the door burst open and in scampered the enormous dog with eyes as large as saucers. The soldier jumped up and looked round for the blue apron, but he had no need to be alarmed.

"What commands do you have for me, Master?" asked the dog.

"Commands? Ah, now I understand why the witch wanted the box so much," said the soldier smiling. "Fetch me some money, quickly!"

At that the dog vanished, but a moment

later he reappeared, carrying in his mouth a large bag of copper coins.

Now very soon the soldier had mastered the tricks of the tinderbox. If he struck the flint once he got the copper-coin dog. If he struck it twice he got the silver-coin dog, while the gold-coin dog came in answer to three strikes of the flint.

Within a day the soldier was back in his princely lodgings. This time, however, he was sure he knew how to see the princess. He struck the flint once, and when the dog appeared he commanded:

"Bring the princess of this city to me immediately!"

No sooner said than done! In a minute or two the dog returned, carrying on his back the princess, fast asleep. She looked so beautiful that the soldier could not resist kissing her. Then the dog took her back to the palace.

Next morning the princess told her parents how she had dreamed that an enormous dog had carried her away and a soldier had kissed her. Well, her parents didn't like the sound of that at all, so that night they had a watch set over their daughter.

When the soldier ordered the dog to bring the princess to him again, the animal was followed all the way back to the soldier's lodgings. In fact, the old woman who followed the dog drew a white cross with a chalk on the door of the house, and only quick thinking by the dog himself prevented the secret from reaching the king. For the dog noticed the chalk cross, and quickly rushed back along the street putting a cross on all the doors!

That spoiled the king's plan, but the queen had another. She made a little purse for her daughter which she filled with flour so that when, on the third night running, the dog carried the princess off to the soldier, the purse left a trail of flour which was very easy to follow.

Next thing the poor soldier knew, he was clapped in prison and condemned to be hanged. Worst of all, he had been marched off so quickly that his tinderbox was left behind. As the day of his execution drew near, the soldier began to despair of rescue.

Then, on the very morning, as the crowd gathered to watch his execution, the soldier, craning out of his prison window, managed to attract the attention of a shoemaker's son.

"Look—I've no time to explain, but if you want to earn yourself sixpence, just run to my lodgings and bring me the tinderbox you will find there."

To the soldier's joy and relief the shoemaker's son was indeed very pleased to earn sixpence, and did exactly as he was asked.

When the soldier mounted the gibbet before the whole population of the city, including the king, the queen, the beautiful princess and all the government, he cried out:

"Your Majesty, before you hang me grant me this final request: that I may smoke one last pipe of tobacco!"

Well, that seemed a reasonable enough thing to ask. So the king gave his assent, and the soldier was unchained.

In a flash he struck flint and steel together once, twice, three times—and instantly all three enormous dogs appeared together.

"Master, what is your request?" they asked together.

"Help me—don't let me be hanged!" cried the soldier.

Quickly, the three monstrous dogs disposed of the king and queen, the government and the judges, tossing them away into the air. Then the crowd that had come to watch the soldier being hanged began to cheer him instead, and very soon it was settled that he should become the new king, with the lovely princess as his queen.

The wedding festivities lasted a whole week and the three dogs were there to watch everything, opening their enormous eyes even wider than usual at the beauty and splendour of everything they saw.